Mosby's Workbook for Nursing Assistants

Mosby's Workbook for Nursing Assistants

Relda Timmeney Kelly, RN, MSN

With contributions from
CherylAnn Smith Owoc, RN, MSN, MEd

Fourth Edition
with 134 illustrations

Mosby Lifeline

St. Louis Baltimore Boston Carlsbad Chicago Naples New York Philadelphia Portland
London Madrid Mexico City Singapore Sydney Tokyo Toronto Wiesbaden

Mosby Lifeline
Dedicated to Publishing Excellence

Managing Editor: Doris E. Smith
Assistant Editor: Elaine M. Wilburt
Project Manager: Christopher J. Baumle
Production Editor: David Orzechowski
Interior Design: Ellen Dawson
Design Manager: Nancy McDonald

Fourth edition

Printed in the United States of America
Mosby–Year Book, Inc.
11830 Westline Industrial Drive
St. Louis, Missouri 63146

ISBN 0-8151-5057-1
TCS/VH 10 9 8 7 6

Illustration Credits

Chapter 5
5–1 a–c from Austrin M, Austrin H: *Learning medical terminology, ed 8,* St Louis, 1995, Mosby–Year Book.
5–2 from Seeley R, Stephens T, Tate P: *Anatomy and Physiology, ed 3,* St Louis, 1995, Mosby–Year Book.

Chapter 20
20–1 a–f from *Wong D: Whaley and Wong's essentials of pediatric nursing, ed 4,* St Louis, 1993, Mosby–Year Book.

DEDICATION

To my first grandchild—

Samuel Brooks Donavon

He has made me aware of the continuum of life. He is my link to the past and my connection to the future.

PREFACE

The fourth edition of Mosby's Workbook for Nursing Assistants is a companion study guide for Mosby's Textbook for Nursing Assistants. The workbook contains a variety of exercises for each chapter to give students with different learning styles choices to study the chapter and master the information.

Each chapter of the workbook has two major sections with the following content:

- PERSONAL EXPLORATIONS This section contains several projects related to the chapter designed to explore personal feelings, apply new knowledge in a simulated situation, or to develop new skills through practical application. Some exercises are designed for a group of students to work together and others may be done by the individual student.
- CAREER PREPARATIONS This section contains a variety of exercises to review the chapter content. The exercises vary from chapter to chapter. Included are Crosswords, Word Searches, Word Scrambles, Riddles, Labeling, Choose the Correct Answer, Matching, Fill-in-the-Blanks, and True/False Statements.

The fourth edition has been revised in several areas. The Personal Explorations exercises are new or have been revised to give the student more guidance in carrying them out. Each contains questions to lead the student to utilize critical thinking skills in completing the exercise. New questions and exercises have been added in Career Preparations to include new content and to expand the opportunities for learning. True/False statements require the student to correct any false statement to a true statement. A new 100 point comprehensive final examination is found at the end of the book. This test will help to prepare the student for comprehensive testing for course completion and certification.

Answers to the Career Preparations sections and the final examination are included in the Instructor's Guide. This gives the instructor the choice of giving the student these answers for self-evaluation or using the exercises as review or homework assignments. Answers are not given for the Personal Explorations sections. Often the questions asked do not have a clear right or wrong choice; rather, they encourage the student to think through the situation. The instructor may wish to use these exercises for classroom discussion, allowing students to share various points of view on the topic.

This edition could not have been compiled without the assistance of assistant editor Elaine Wilburt. Her encouragement and creativity challenged me to reach higher to achieve the expectations and vision she had for the workbook. Thanks to Cheryl Owoc for contributing many of the creative exercises in the Career Preparations section. A special thanks to Sheila Sorrentino for asking me to write the first workbook over ten years ago. I have learned so much from being involved in this project over the years. As with previous editions, I could not have carried out this revision without the constant support of my husband, Earl. He patiently tolerated my many weekends and evenings spent at the computer and kept the household running! Finally, a salute to my "co-author," Bogart—who slept on my papers, walked across the keyboard and was a constant companion who provided comfort and solace when things bogged down.

CONTENTS

Mosby's *Workbook* *for* *Nursing* *Assistants*

1

Introduction to Health Care Facilities

PERSONAL EXPLORATIONS

1 Answer these questions about health care facilities in your area.

- How many hospitals are located in your area? How many beds are available in each one?
- How many long-term care facilities do you have in your area? Do they accept all types of patients (for example, by the level of care needed, the disease category, the method of payment for services)? How many beds does each one have?
- Find out if you have a mental health care hospital in your area. If there are no mental health hospitals, where do people with mental illness receive care?
- Do you have home health or hospice care agencies in your area? What are their names? Are they connected to area hospitals or do they operate independently?

2 Who do you know that works in a health care position? What is the person's position? How many years of schooling did the person need to prepare for this position? What future plans does the person have to continue his/her education?

CAREER PREPARATIONS

Matching

Match the following statements with one of the types of health care services.

- **a** Hospital
- **b** Subacute care
- **c** Long-term care
- **d** Mental health care
- **e** Home care agencies
- **f** Hospice

1 ______ Serves people who are dying

2 ______ Provides services to persons who do not need hospital care but cannot care for themselves at home

3 ______ Serves people of all ages for acute, chronic, or terminal illnesses

4 ______ Treats people who may have difficulty dealing with life

5 ______ Serves people who may need rehabilitation and some care after hospitalization

6 ______ Provides services to people who need assistance with care at home

Match the following statements with one of the methods of organizing nursing care.

- **a** Functional nursing
- **b** Team nursing
- **c** Primary nursing
- **d** Case management

7 _____ One RN is responsible for the person's care on a 24-hour basis.

8 _____ One RN coordinates care with the person's doctor and community agencies.

9 _____ Assignments for care are made according to the person's needs and the skills of the workers.

10 _____ Each member of the nursing team is assigned specific tasks to do for all patients.

11 _____ An RN may work only with persons who have similar health problems.

True or False

Read each statement and circle "T" if it is true, "F" if it is false. If the statement is false, in the space beneath the statement, change the words to make the statement true.

12 T F A variety of workers who work together to provide health care for patients are members of the nursing team.

____

13 T F Health care systems involve health care agencies joining together as one provider of care.

____

14 T F The nursing assistant reports to the nursing supervisor.

____

15 T F Educational programs for nursing personnel are taught by doctors.

____

16 T F The nursing team involves RNs, LPNs, and nursing assistants.

____

17 T F An LPN studies for 2 to 3 years to complete a nursing program.

____

18 T F Low income families may be eligible for health insurance through Medicaid.

____

Choose the Correct Answer

Circle the letter next to the statement that best completes the sentence or answers the question.

19 The goal of health promotion is to

- **a** reduce the risk of illness.
- **b** prevent diseases by healthy living and good health care.
- **c** look for causes and cures of diseases.
- **d** detect diseases by observing signs and symptoms.

20 Rehabilitation begins when a person

- **a** goes home.
- **b** can function without help.
- **c** first receives health care.
- **d** has had tests to diagnose the disease.

21 Who is responsible for the coordination of care on the health team?

- **a** Doctor
- **b** Family member
- **c** Registered Nurse
- **d** Director of Nursing

22 Diagnosis related groups (DRGs) determine the cost of hospital care

- **a** before care is given.
- **b** based on the person's ability to pay.
- **c** after the hospital stay.
- **d** based on how much insurance the person has purchased.

Riddle

Read the statements and solve the riddle.

23 What am I? ____________________

- I was passed by Congress in 1987.
- One of my purposes is to improve the quality of care given to residents of nursing facilities.
- I require that nursing assistants receive at least 75 hours of instruction and successfully pass a competency evaluation.
- I outline the rights of residents in nursing facilities.

Labeling

Fill in members of the nursing department on the organizational chart in Figure 1-1.

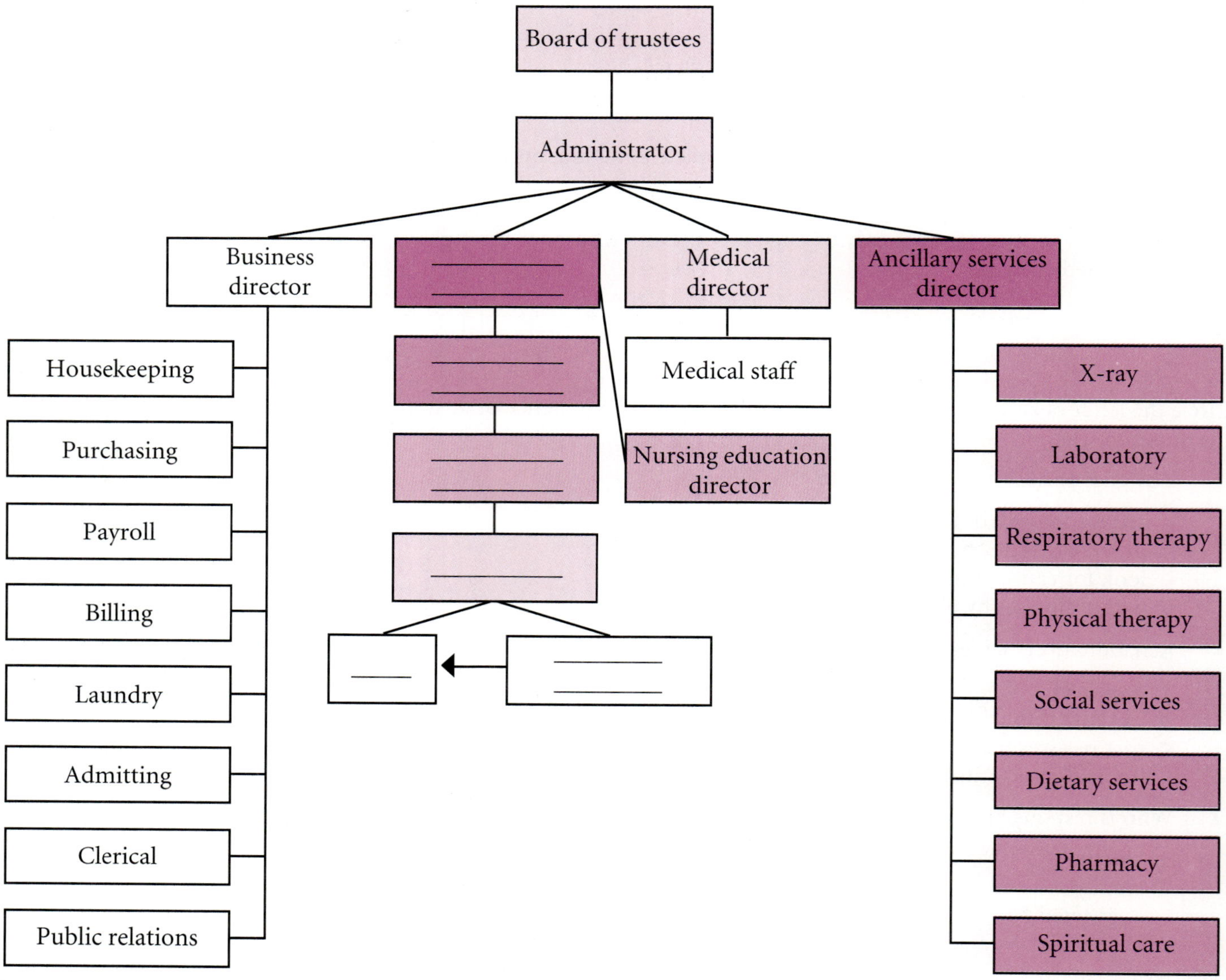

Fig. 1-1 *Organizational chart.*

24 What are the two groups in Figure 1-1 to whom the nursing assistant reports?

a ______________________

b ______________________

25 On Figure 1-2, identify the members of the health care team. List one of the services provided to patients/residents by each team member.

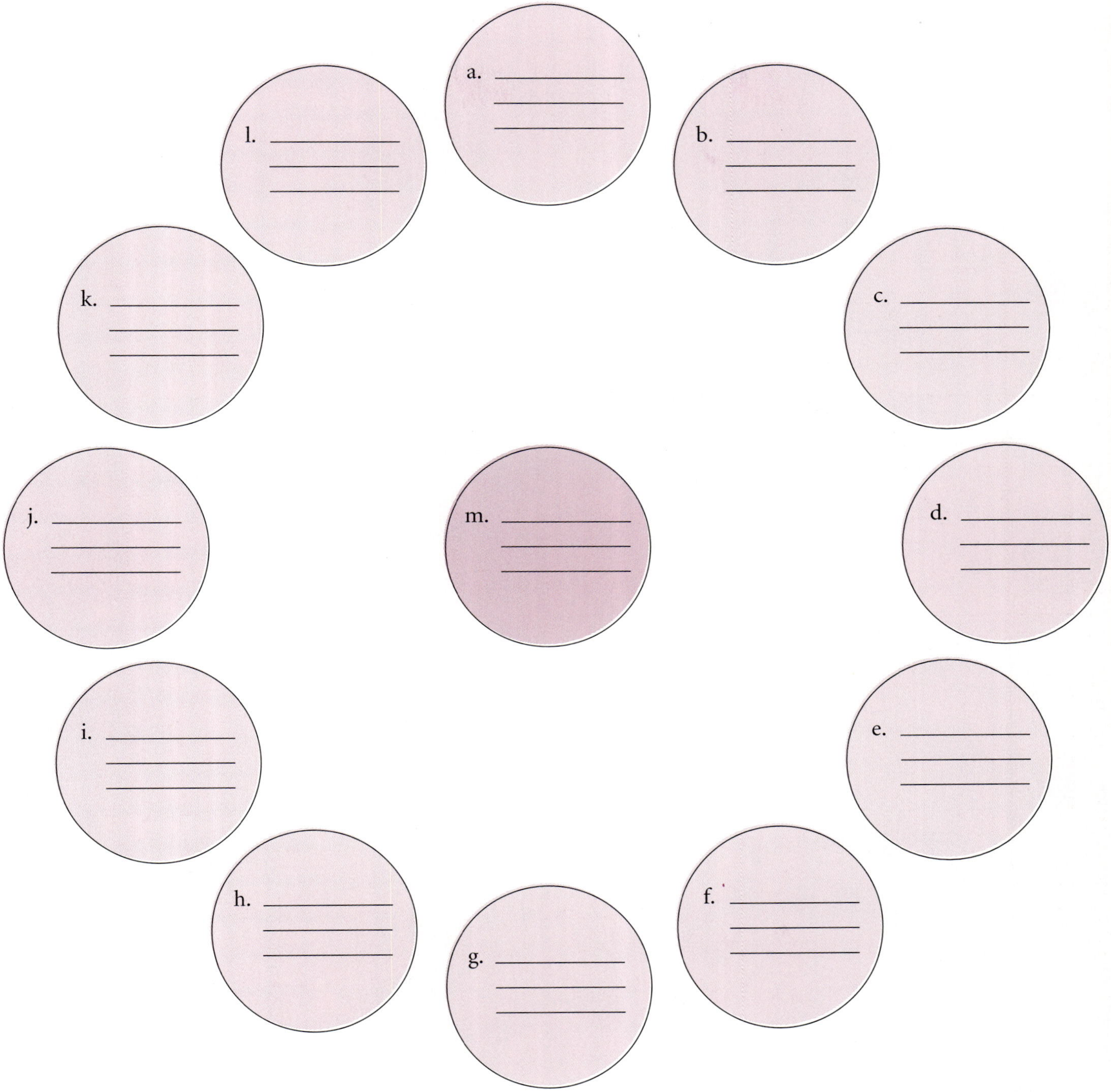

Fig. 1-2 *The health care team.*

2 The Nursing Assistant

PERSONAL EXPLORATIONS

1 How would you feel about performing duties that conflict with your own moral or religious beliefs? What duties would make you uncomfortable?

2 Role play a situation in which you are asked to perform one of the duties you identified above. Have one student play the person asking you to perform the task, and have a second student act as an observer to answer the following questions:

- How did you communicate your discomfort with the task?
- What was your reaction when asked?
- What suggestions were made to solve this problem? (What ways were used to see that the task was completed? What did you offer to do to help ?)

3 Why do you feel you will be a good nursing assistant? What qualities and characteristics do you have that will be helpful? How can you improve qualities and characteristics that you feel are weaknesses?

4 What area or areas would interest you if your employer asks you to cross train? Why does this area appeal to you?

5 What health practices that you follow will help you set a good example for others? What practices should you try to improve?

6 Have you ever applied for a job? How did you feel when you were being interviewed? After reading this chapter, in what ways could you improve future interviews?

7 How many facilities in your area employ nursing assistants? Which of these places require nursing assistants to be certified? What is a typical starting salary?

8 Who are three people you could ask to give their names as references when applying for a job? Make a list of these people and their titles, addresses, and telephone numbers to use when you apply for a job.

CAREER PREPARATIONS

Fill-in-the-Blanks

Fill in the word or phrase that best completes the sentence or answers the question.

1 If you do not understand directions or instructions, you should ____________ ____.

2 If the nurse asks you to give medications to a person, you should respectfully and firmly ____.

3 ________________ are legally responsible for supervising nursing assistants.

4 When you address people by a title and name ("Mr. Johnson"), you are showing ____.

5 You should not wear strong perfume, cologne, or aftershave lotion because ____.

6 If a patient complains of chest pain and you do not report this to the nurse, this is a ____ act.

7 Discussing a person's treatment with your best friend invades a person's ____.

The following statements describe acts committed by a person against another person or property. These acts are called torts; they can be intentional or unintentional. Write in the space what tort has been committed and circle I if it was intentional or U for unintentional.

8 I U ______________________ While cleaning a person's dentures, the nursing assistant drops and breaks them.

9 I U ______________________ A nursing assistant opens a person's mail and reads it.

10 I U ______________________ Instead of allowing the person a choice, the nursing assistant tells him/her that he/she will get a shower whether he/she wants one or not.

11 I U ____________________ A person put his/her signal light on 20 minutes ago. The person tries to go to the bathroom alone, slips and falls, and breaks a hip.

12 I U ____________________ A nursing assistant talks to employees from other departments about a person.

13 I U ____________________ After morning care is completed, a person wants to go to activities. The nursing assistant does not allow the person to go.

14 I U ____________________ An individual has failed to act in a reasonable and careful manner and caused harm to the person or property of another.

15 I U ____________________ An individual has injured the name and reputation of a person by making false statements to a third person.

16 I U ____________________ An individual attempts or threatens to touch a person's body without the person's consent.

17 I U ____________________ An individual touches a person's body without the person's consent.

18 I U ____________________ An individual exposes the private affairs of a person to a third person.

19 I U ____________________ An individual tricks or fools another person.

20 I U ____________________ An individual restrains or restricts a person's freedom of movement without a physician's order.

Choose the Correct Answer

Circle the letter next to the statement that best completes the sentence or answers the question.

21 Your work is supervised by

a a nurse.
b the doctor.
c the Director of Nursing.
d a nursing assistant with more experience.

22 OBRA requires that you retrain and pass a new competency test if you have not worked as a certified nursing assistant for

a 2 consecutive years.
b 5 years.
c 1 consecutive year.
d 6 months.

23 You feel ill this morning and are scheduled to work. Which action is correct?

- **a** Stay in bed. Your supervisor knew you were not feeling well yesterday and will assume you are not coming in today.
- **b** Go to work. The other nursing assistants and the nurse are depending on you.
- **c** Call the facility as early as possible. Explain the reason for your absence.
- **d** Call when you wake up as long as it is before your shift ends. Explain why you were absent.

24 Which of the following actions is *not* good conduct for a nursing assistant?

- **a** Carrying out any assignment given to you by the nurse
- **b** Taking only the drugs that have been prescribed by the doctor
- **c** Recognizing the limits of your role and your knowledge
- **d** Considering the patient's needs to be more important than your needs

25 As a nursing assistant, you may be asked to cross-train. One skill you would *not* be asked to learn would be

- **a** developing the care plan for a person.
- **b** drawing blood samples.
- **c** performing EKGs.
- **d** learning physical therapy techniques.

26 Cross-training is a trend mostly because it

- **a** keeps employees busy.
- **b** reduces the number of people caring for a patient.
- **c** reduces infections.
- **d** gives more people jobs.

27 When going to an interview it would be appropriate to

- **a** have a glass of wine before arriving to relax.
- **b** wear a sweatsuit and athletic shoes to show that you are physically fit.
- **c** wear no perfume or aftershave lotion.
- **d** arrive exactly at the time of the interview so you do not have time to get nervous.

28 When planning and organizing your work, it is acceptable to

- **a** interrupt a person's meal to give a bath so you keep on schedule.
- **b** make a list of procedures and tasks that must be done on a schedule.
- **c** work by yourself at all times so that you do not interfere with another worker's schedule.
- **d** wait until the end of the shift when you are not so busy to carry out care and treatments.

29 If you are asked to obtain a person's signature on an informed consent, you should

- **a** make sure the person is mentally competent.
- **b** refuse because this is not a nursing assistant responsibility.
- **c** ask a family member to witness the signature.
- **d** call the doctor to come and witness the signature.

Legal terms

Crossword

ACROSS

2. Intentionally attempting to touch the body of another person without permission
5. What is right and wrong conduct
8. Rule of conduct made by a government body
10. Act that is a violation of criminal law
11. Negligence by a professional person
12. Wrong committed against another person or the person's property

DOWN

1. Actual unauthorized touching of another person's body without consent
3. Defamation through written statements
4. Unintentional wrong in which a person fails to act in a reasonable and careful manner
6. Defamation through oral statements
7. Injuring the reputation of another person by making false statements to a third person
9. Legal statement of how an individual wishes to have property distributed after death.

3 Communicating in the Health Care Facility

PERSONAL EXPLORATIONS

1 CASE STUDY: Mr. Smith had abdominal surgery yesterday. Last evening, he sat on the edge of the bed for a short time. This morning the nursing assistant gave him a bed bath and assisted him to sit in a chair at the bedside. He sat there for 15 minutes while the bed was being made. He sat very still and held his arms tightly across his abdomen. He then was assisted back to bed. He asked to have the head of the bed raised and held a pillow to his abdomen.

Imagine you are Mr. Smith in this situation and answer these questions.

- What would you like the nursing assistant to tell you?
- How would you communicate your feelings to the nursing assistant?
- How could you let the nursing assistant know that you had pain without telling her?

Imagine you are the nursing assistant in this situation and answer these questions.

- As the nursing assistant, what observations would be important to make about Mr. Smith?
- What questions could you ask Mr. Smith?
- What nonverbal communication would give you information about Mr. Smith?

2 Answer these questions about situations in which you may need to communicate with others.

- What situations have you had in which it has been difficult to communicate? Why was it difficult? How did you handle this?
- Think about a situation in which you feel you communicated your point well. What made the communication successful? How could you use a similar technique in caring for patients/residents?
- How would you communicate with a person who speaks a different language? What methods could you use to explain what you are going to do?
- How would you communicate with a person from a different culture?

3 CASE STUDY: Mrs. Miller was admitted to the hospital 3 hours ago. You have just started your shift and have been assigned to Mrs. Miller.

- What information would you need to know before giving care? Why?
- What information would be important to provide to the oncoming shift?
- What methods would you use to communicate this information?

4 It is often difficult to describe fluids in a clear and precise manner. Set up the following examples that imitate situations where you need to describe intake, output, or drainage. Describe, as accurately as possible, what you see in terms of amounts, colors, and textures. Compare your notes with classmates to see if you are using words that have the same meanings. What words were used that were clear to understand? What words were used that had more than one meaning?

- Bloody drainage: Mix a teaspoon of ketchup with a teaspoon of water. Pour onto the center of a paper napkin.
- Urine: Pour a tablespoon of tea into the center of a paper towel.
- Bleeding: Smear a teaspoon of red jelly in the center of a paper towel.
- Broth: Pour 4 ounces of tea into a bowl.

Class Experiment

Substance	Observations
Bloody Drainage	
Urine	
Bleeding	
Broth	

CAREER PREPARATIONS

Matching

Match the following statements with one of the key terms related to communication.

a Nursing care plan
b Nursing diagnosis
c Nursing intervention
d Nursing process
e Medical diagnosis
f MDS
g RAP

1 ______ Identification of a disease or condition by a doctor

2 ______ Form used to assess resident's mental, physical, and psychosocial functions

3 ______ Statement describing a health problem that can be treated by nursing measures

4 ______ Triggers and guidelines used to develop a comprehensive care plan

5 ______ Written guide that gives direction about nursing care a person should receive

6 ______ Method used by nurses to plan and deliver nursing care

7 ______ Action taken by a nursing team member to help a person reach a goal

Choose the Correct Answer

Circle the letter next to the statement that best completes the sentence or answers the question.

8 Circle each statement that is a rule of communication. (Circle *all* correct answers.)

a Use words that have only one meaning.
b Describe very clearly, giving all the details.
c Be specific and concise when giving information.
d Organize information in a logical manner.
e Answers should be general, not specific.

9 The medical record will include all of the following *except*

a a physical examination record.
b a graphic sheet.
c a Kardex.
d X-ray examination reports.
e an admission sheet.

10 If a person asks to see the chart, you should

a give it to him/her, because the person always has a right to see the chart.
b read the chart and tell the person what it says.
c tell the nurse who is responsible for the person's care.
d tell the person that he/she is not allowed to see the chart.

11 What information is *not* included on the graphic sheet?

a Temperature, pulse, and respirations
b Bowel sounds
c Height and weight
d Bowel movements
e Appetite

12 Circle each word that reflects part of the nursing process. (Circle *all* correct answers.)

a Assessment
b History
c Implementation
d Analysis
e Evaluation

13 Another name for the clues in the MDS is

a signs.
b triggers.
c symptoms.
d diagnosis.

14 The purpose of a care conference is to

a identify the medical diagnosis.
b develop or devise a person's nursing care plan for effective care.
c share the end-of-shift report.
d chart day-to-day care of the person.

Fill-in-the-Blanks

Fill in the word or phrase that best completes the sentence or answers the question.

15 What are the four senses you use to obtain information about a person?

a ______________________________

b ______________________________

c ______________________________

d ______________________________

16 When a person tells you about pains or problems you cannot observe through your senses, they are called symptoms or ________________ data.

17 When you can obtain information about a person with your senses, it is called signs or ________________ data.

18 Each of the following is either subjective or objective data. In the blank next to each statement, place an S for subjective or an O for objective.

a ______ Sleepy
b ______ Chest pain
c ______ Skin cool
d ______ Cyanosis of nails
e ______ Labored breathing
f ______ Gas pain
g ______ Pain when urinating
h ______ Productive cough
i ______ Breath has fruity odor
j ______ Pulse rapid

19 The following statements are either subjective or objective data. Place an S for a subjective statement or an O for an objective statement.

a ______ Mr. Jones states he is cold.
b ______ Mary has red hair.
c ______ Mrs. Smith says she has pain in her right shoulder.
d ______ Temperature 99.6° F, pulse 72, respirations 16
e ______ Mr. Green ate all of his breakfast.
f ______ Mrs. Foster says she is anxious about having surgery.

20 Next to each of the following write the time using the 24 hour clock.

a ______ 11:00 AM
b ______ 8:00 AM
c ______ 4:00 PM
d ______ 7:30 AM
e ______ 6:45 PM
f ______ 12 NOON
g ______ 3:00 AM
h ______ 4:50 AM
i ______ 5:30 PM
j ______ 10:45 PM
k ______ 11:55 PM
l ______ 9:15 PM

21 When you write entries in the chart you sign your name and

______________.

Riddle

Read the statements and solve the riddle.

22 What am I? ______________________

- I cannot be seen, heard, or felt.
- I am subjective.
- I may last a short time or longer than 6 months.
- I can radiate from the site of tissue damage to nearby areas.
- I may be felt in a body part that is no longer there.
- Each person reacts to me differently.

Diagrams

23 In the portions of the chart provided in Figure 3-1, identify where you would find the following information:

a Birth date ____________________

b Intake and output ____________________

c Observations about a person's condition ____________________

d Religion ____________________

e Diet order ____________________

f Bowel movements ____________________

g Description of nursing care given ____________________

h Activity order ____________________

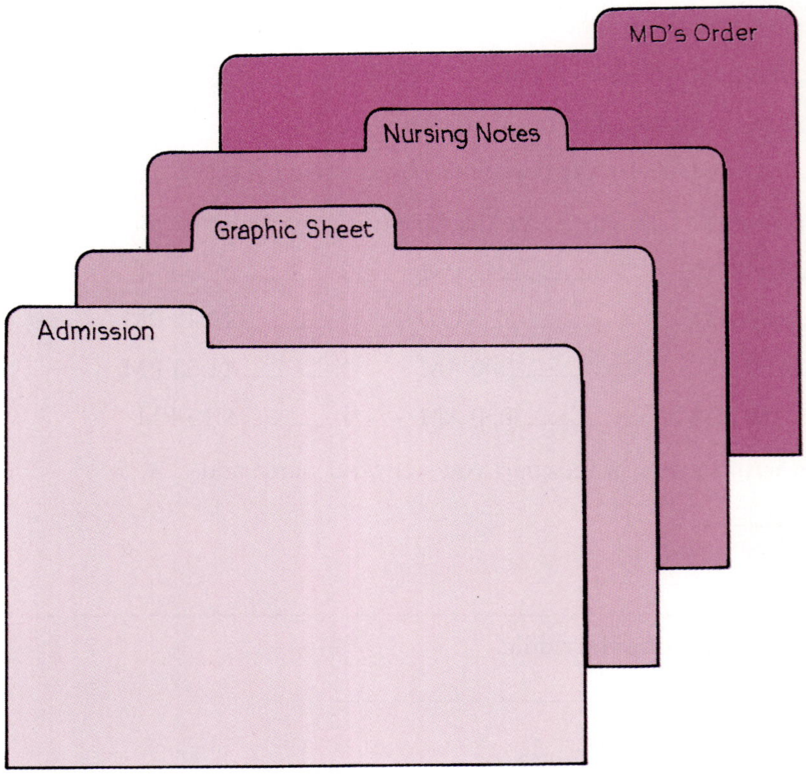

Fig. 3-1 *Patient/resident chart.*

24 Using Figure 3-2 as a guide, convert the following times from 24-hour clock time to standard time and from standard time to 24-hour clock time as indicated.

a 2:00 AM ______	**e** 0600 hrs ______	AM/PM (circle one)
b 10:30 AM ______	**f** 1145 hrs ______	AM/PM (circle one)
c 5:00 AM ______	**g** 1800 hrs ______	AM/PM (circle one)
d 9:30 AM ______	**h** 2200 hrs ______	AM/PM (circle one)

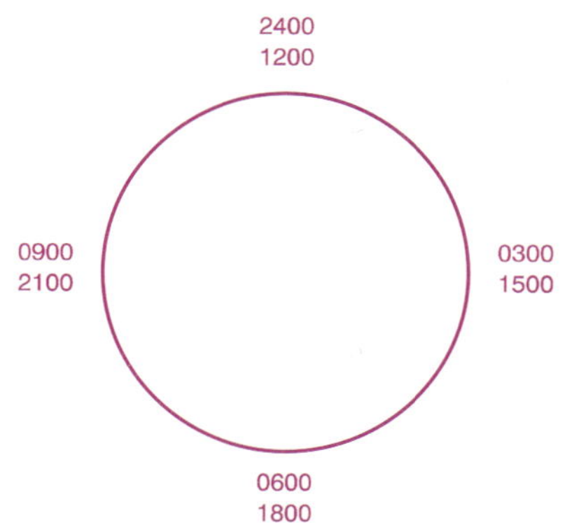

Fig. 3-2 *The 24-hour clock.*

4 Understanding the Persons You Care For

PERSONAL EXPLORATIONS

1 Reread the section of your textbook in Chapter 4 about Maslow's hierarchy of needs. Use these questions to identify how you meet your own basic needs.

- Do you smoke? If so, how does that affect your breathing?
- What kinds of foods and fluids do you eat? Is your diet meeting your basic need for food and water?
- How much rest do you get each day?
- How safe do you feel at home? At school? In your community? How do your feelings affect your ability to hold a job or go to school?
- Who are the people who make you feel loved? Who helps you when you have problems?
- What basic need is being met when you attend school or develop new skills?

2 Answer these questions about your personal health care practices.

- What health care practices are followed in your family? How are these practices related to your cultural or religious beliefs?
- How often do you go to the doctor? For regular checkups? Only when ill?
- When do you go to the dentist? Once or twice a year for cleaning and checkup? Only when you have a toothache?
- How often does a pregnant woman visit the doctor? All during the pregnancy? After 6 months? Does she first seek help when in labor?
- When do infants in the family go to the doctor or clinic? For regular well-baby visits?

Only when immunizations must be done for school requirements?

- When a family member is hospitalized, how does the family respond? Does someone stay with the person and administer all of the care? Does the family visit for brief periods and let health care workers provide all care?

CAREER PREPARATIONS

Word Search

Find the word in Chapter 4 of the textbook that matches each definition. Write it next to the correct definition. Circle or highlight the words in the puzzle.

1 ______________________ Disease that lasts a short time

2 ______________________ Disease that lasts a long time, possibly the rest of the person's life

3 ______________________ Special unit in a hospital that cares for a person with acute heart or cardiovascular diseases

4 ______________________ Hospital area that first treats persons who are injured or who have sudden medical problems

5 ______________________ Branch of medicine concerned with problems and diseases of the elderly

6 ______________________ Special unit in a hospital that cares for patients with kidney or renal failure

7 ______________________ Persons who are ill with diseases or conditions that do not require surgery

8 ______________________ Branch of medicine that cares for women during and immediately after pregnancy

9 ______________________ Branch of medicine that cares for children from birth, usually through adolescence

10 ______________________ Branch of medicine that cares for persons who have mental health problems

11 ______________________ Persons who are being prepared for or who have had surgery

12 ______________________ Approaching death

S	R	Q	I	V	B	A	C	T	W	E	D	S	R	X	A	E	W
O	P	S	Y	C	H	I	A	T	R	Y	E	W	O	R	K	E	R
R	U	T	S	X	N	A	C	E	P	E	R	O	A	W	A	K	E
D	R	O	F	E	A	R	U	A	A	O	B	R	A	Y	R	I	A
E	U	R	O	M	C	T	T	R	I	B	E	D	M	O	A	D	T
S	L	A	M	E	E	Y	E	S	N	S	K	I	U	T	R	N	H
T	E	A	R	R	P	E	D	I	A	T	R	I	C	S	L	E	M
O	N	N	K	G	C	E	B	O	C	E	J	L	O	H	A	Y	N
R	T	U	L	E	J	G	K	V	W	T	T	L	U	A	Y	D	A
C	H	R	O	N	I	C	U	A	A	R	O	M	S	P	T	I	S
L	A	S	T	C	A	D	T	R	V	I	B	O	Y	E	S	A	T
O	R	I	N	Y	S	U	R	G	I	C	A	L	N	O	A	L	R
T	O	N	E	R	S	O	R	D	E	S	X	D	A	I	S	Y	B
H	I	G	O	O	D	O	G	T	E	R	M	I	N	A	L	S	Z
I	N	A	G	O	R	A	L	E	S	O	I	L	E	D	E	I	N
N	E	S	T	M	E	D	I	C	A	L	B	A	G	V	E	S	T
G	O	S	B	E	D	A	B	A	T	H	S	S	T	O	P	A	C
M	A	T	E	C	O	R	O	N	A	R	Y	C	A	R	E	P	C
O	B	S	E	R	V	E	K	R	E	A	D	O	B	Y	I	X	D
R	U	S	T	Y	A	X	B	Y	O	P	U	A	O	T	I	C	S
E	T	R	O	B	N	R	O	E	A	R	G	T	U	R	N	E	S

13 Label Figure 4-1 with the basic needs for life as described by Abraham Maslow. Then place each of the following needs in the appropriate space: **Diagram**

- Explaining why a procedure is to be done
- Visiting with friends
- Helping a woman put on her makeup
- Making a bird house for a grandson
- Helping a man put a nasal cannula in place

Fig. 4-1 *Maslow's Hierarchy of Needs.*

Matching

Match one of Maslow's hierarchy of needs with each of the words or phrases.

a Physiological
b Safety and security
c Love and belonging
d Self-esteem
e Self-actualization

14 ______ Clothing

15 ______ Closeness

16 ______ Experiencing one's potential

17 ______ Food

18 ______ Protection from harm

19 ______ Affection

20 ______ Water

21 ______ Meaningful relationships

22 ______ Rest

23 ______ Elimination

24 ______ Opinion of self

25 ______ Shelter

Match the country with a belief or practice that may be followed by people from that country.

a Poland
b Former Soviet Union
c Philippines
d Mexico
e India
f Mainland China
g Vietnam

26 ______ Males are viewed as being healthier than females and children.

27 ______ Health and illness are not separated, but are part of a lifelong continuum.

28 ______ Medicine to restore yin-yang is important.

29 ______ Ghosts and spirits control life and death.

30 ______ Wearing religious medals or scapulars helps protect them against illness.

31 ______ Three kisses on cheek for greeting or farewell is common.

32 ______ Men will not shake hands with women. Instead they place palms together and bow.

33 ______ Family decisions overrule decisions made by health care workers.

Fill-in-the-Blanks

Fill in the word or phrase that best completes the sentence or answers the question.

34 The branch of medicine concerned with the care of women during pregnancy, labor, and childbirth, and during the 6 to 8 weeks after birth is called ______________________.

35 ______________________ is the branch of medicine concerned with the growth, development, and care of children ranging in age from newborn to adolescent.

36 ______________________ patients are usually adults with illnesses, diseases, or injuries that do not need surgery.

37 ______________________ patients are being prepared for or have had simple or very complex surgery.

38 ______________________ is the branch of medicine concerned with the diagnosis and treatment of people with mental health problems that may vary from mild to severe mental and emotional disorders.

39 ______________________ is the branch of medicine concerned with the problems and diseases of old age and the elderly. It includes the changes that occur normally from aging as well as the acute, chronic or degenerative diseases common in the elderly.

40 When someone is sick and cannot perform daily activities themselves, he/she may react by becoming frustrated and ______________________.

41 When you hold a person's hand or touch the shoulder to convey caring or warmth, you are using ______________________ communication.

42 A person who denies having pain but protects a body part by lying in a certain way is using ______________________ language to communicate.

43 If a nursing assistant shows distaste for a body odor by wrinkling his/her nose or frowning, his/her ______________________ is sending a message through body language.

44 If a nursing assistant tells a person "Don't worry" or "Everything will be OK," this may be a ______________________ to effective communication.

45 What types of effective communication are used in these statements?

a ______________________ "You don't understand why it hurts so much since your surgery."

b ______________________ "What time did you go to physical therapy?"

c ______________________ "Tell me what you do when you are working."

d ______________________ "Could you explain again where the pain is located?"

46 In each of these examples, which section of the Patients' Bill of Rights is represented?

a The nursing assistant refuses to answer her family's questions about a friend who is hospitalized.

____

b The student nurse introduces himself and identifies the school he attends.

____

c The nurse makes sure that the person is given instructions to call the doctor for an appointment before she discharges the person.

____

d The nursing assistant explains to the person and his family when visiting hours are scheduled.

____

e The nursing assistant uses the person's given name instead of a nickname such as "Grandma."

____

f The nurse explains what procedure will be done before having the person sign a consent form.

____

g The nursing assistant pulls a curtain while giving a bed bath.

____

h The person is transferred to another hospital because he needs a special test that is not available in this hospital.

____

i The doctor asks the person for permission to use an experimental drug.

____

j The person questions several charges on her bill.

____

k Before applying the cuff, the nursing assistant tells the person she is going to take her blood pressure.

____

l The person tells the doctor he will not have open heart surgery, which the doctor recommends.

____

Word Jumbler

Unscramble the terms and use the circled letters to make a word that completes the sentence.

47 a S H O P A I L T   V E S R I C E S

○ _ _ _ _ _ _ _   _ ○ _ _ _ _ _ _

b V A P R I C Y

○ _ _ _ ○ _ _

c F R O M A I N T O I N

○ _ _ _ _ _ _ _ ○ _ _

d L O N D I F I C E N T A I T Y

_ _ ○ _ _ _ _ _ _ _ _ _ _ ○ _

e S N O C E R I D I O N T A

_ _ _ _ _ ○ _ _ _ _ _ _ _

f S E R T E P C

○ _ _ _ _ _ _

g M O N F I R E D   S N O C N E T

_ _ _ _ _ _ _ _   _ _ _ ○ _ _ _

h F R E U S I N G   M R E A T E N T T

_ _ _ _ _ _ _ ○   _ _ _ _ ○ _ _ _ _

i This came about in 1973, when people demanded more information about their health problems and treatment.

_ _ _ _ _ _ _   _ _ _ _ _ _

5

Body Structure and Function

PERSONAL EXPLORATIONS

1 Use your own body and move joints of each type to see how they move.

- Which joint did you use for a ball and socket?
- Which joint moved like a hinge?
- Which joint did you move in a pivot motion?

2 Listen to your heartbeat using a stethoscope. Find a pulse in your wrist to feel the blood being pumped through an artery.

3 Listen to a friend's chest with a stethoscope. What sound do you hear? What is making that sound?

4 Have you ever heard your "stomach growl" or heard gurgling noises in your abdomen when you are sitting quietly? What makes that sound? What is the medical term for this action? Listen to your lower abdomen with a stethoscope to hear the sounds.

5 Look at a friend's eye in a dimly lit room and observe the size of the pupils. Now shine a light in the eye. What happens to the pupil? What happens when you move the light away from the eye?

NOTE: Students are responsible only for those terms mentioned in the text. Additional terms used in labeling figures throughout this chapter are for illustrative purposes only.

CAREER PREPARATIONS

Crossword

Body structure

ACROSS

2. Part of the brain that regulates and coordinates body movement
5. Type of muscle that can be consciously controlled
6. Point at which two bones meet
7. Blood cells that protect the body from infection
8. Part of the eye that varies in size with the amount of light
10. Type of muscle found only in the heart

DOWN

1. Involuntary muscle found in many body organs
2. Part of the brain that is the center of thought and intelligence
3. Part of the brain that controls heart rate and breathing
4. Blood cells that help the blood clot
8. Portion of the blood that is mostly water
9. Blood cells that carry oxygen

Matching

Match the following statements with the correct term.

a Artery
b Capillary
c Cell
d Digestion
e Metabolism
f Organ
g Peristalsis
h System
i Tissue
j Vein

1 ______ Blood vessel that carries blood away from the heart

2 ______ Blood vessel that carries blood back to the heart

3 ______ Tiny blood vessel that allows food, oxygen, and other substances to pass to the cells

4 ______ Basic unit of body structure

5 ______ Group of cells with the same function

6 ______ Group of tissues with the same function

7 ______ Organs that work together to perform special functions

8 ______ Process of physically and chemically breaking down food so it can be absorbed for use by the cells of the body

9 ______ Muscle contractions in the digestive system that move food through the alimentary canal

10 ______ Burning of food for heat and energy by the cells

Place an S in front of the statements that describe a function of the skin. Place an M in front of the statements that describe a function of the musculoskeletal system.

11 ______ Provides a framework

12 ______ Provides a protective covering

13 ______ Regulates body temperature

14 ______ Allows the body to move

15 ______ Gives the body shape

16 ______ Has nerve endings that allow the body to sense pleasant and unpleasant stimulation

Match the following statements with one of the terms related to the digestive and urinary systems.

a Bladder	**g** Liver
b Chyme	**h** Meatus
c Colon	**i** Nephrons
d Duodenum	**j** Pancreas
e Jejunum	**k** Saliva
f Kidney	**l** Urethra

17 ______ Structure that adds digestive juices to chyme

18 ______ Semi-liquid food mixture formed in stomach

19 ______ Portion of GI tract that absorbs food

20 ______ Portion of GI tract that absorbs water

21 ______ Produces digestive juices

22 ______ Produces bile

23 ______ Basic working unit of the kidney

24 ______ Hollow muscular sac that stores urine

25 ______ Structure that allows urine to pass from the bladder

26 ______ Opening from the bladder at the end of the urethra

27 ______ Bean-shaped structure that produces urine

28 ______ Moistens food particles in the mouth

Match the action of the hormone with the correct hormone.

a Epinephrine	**d** Parathormone
b Estrogen	**e** Testosterone
c Insulin	**f** Thyroxine

29 ______ Released by pancreas and regulates sugar in blood

30 ______ Sex hormone secreted by testes

31 ______ Sex hormone secreted by ovaries

32 ______ Regulates metabolism

33 ______ Regulates calcium levels in body

34 ______ Stimulates body to produce energy during emergencies

Fill-in-the-Blanks

Fill in the word or phrase that best completes the sentence or answers the question.

35 What are the basic structures of the cell?

a ______________________________

b ______________________________

c ______________________________

36 The process of cell division is called ____________________.

37 What are four basic types of tissue and their functions?

a ______________________________

____

b ______________________________

____

c ______________________________

____

d ______________________________

____

38 What does each type of bone do?

a Long bones ______________________________

b Short bones ______________________________

c Flat bones ______________________________

d Irregular bones ______________________________

39 What movements does each joint make?

a Ball and socket ______________________________

b Hinge ______________________________

c Pivot ______________________________

40 Skeletal muscles are attached to ____________________ and cause ____________________ of body parts.

41 What is the function of the nervous system? ______________________________

42 The pathways that conduct messages to and from the brain are contained in the ____________________.

43 What are the five senses?

a ______________________________

b ______________________________

c ______________________________

d ______________________________

e ______________________________

44 Three small bones in the middle ear ______________ the sound and transmit it to the ______________. They are called the ______________, ______________, and ______________.

45 What are the structures that make up the circulatory system?

a ______________

b ______________

c ______________

46 What is the function of the lungs? ______________

____

47 Describe the function of the digestive system. ______________

____

____

48 The undigested portion of food that passes from the body through the rectum and anus is called ______________.

49 Urine is made up of waste products filtered out of the ______________

______________.

50 What are the functions of the ovaries?

a ______________

b ______________

51 The master gland of the endocrine system is the ______________ gland.

52 What effect do these pituitary hormones have on the body?

a Growth hormone ______________

____

b Thyroid-stimulating hormone (TSH) ______________

____

c Adrenocorticotropic hormone (ACTH) ______________

____

d Antidiuretic hormone (ADH) ______________

____

e Oxytocin ______________

____

53 The major function of the thyroid gland is to regulate

______________.

54 The parathyroid glands are important because they regulate the use of ______________ by the body.

55 What effect do these adrenal hormones have on the body?

a Glucocorticoids ______________________________

____

b Mineralocorticoids ______________________________

____

c Sex hormones ______________________________

____

56 Identify each of the joints in Figure 5-1. Name a joint in the body that moves like each of these joints.

a ______________________________

____

____

b ______________________________

____

____

c ______________________________

____

____

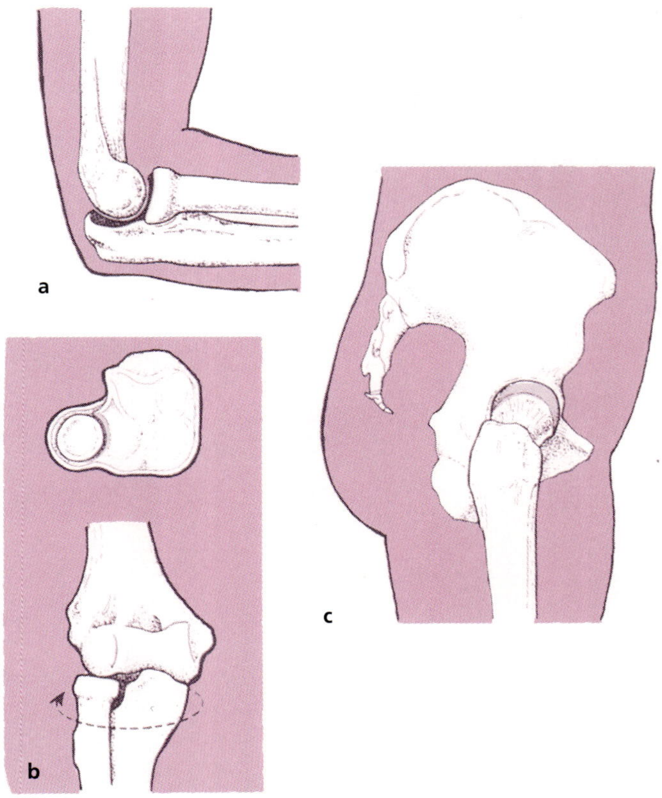

Fig. 5-1 a-c *The joints.*

57 Name the three major parts of the brain indicated in Figure 5-2.

a ____

b ____

c ____

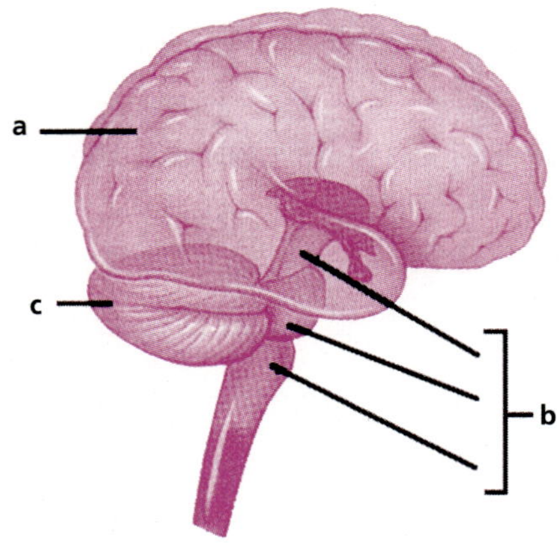

Fig. 5-2 *The brain.*

58 Name the structure and function of the six main parts of the heart indicated in Figure 5-3.

a ______________________________

____

b ______________________________

____

c ______________________________

____

d ______________________________

____

e ______________________________

____

f ______________________________

____

59 Use a red pencil or pen. Using arrows, show the pathway of the blood through the heart in Figure 5-3.

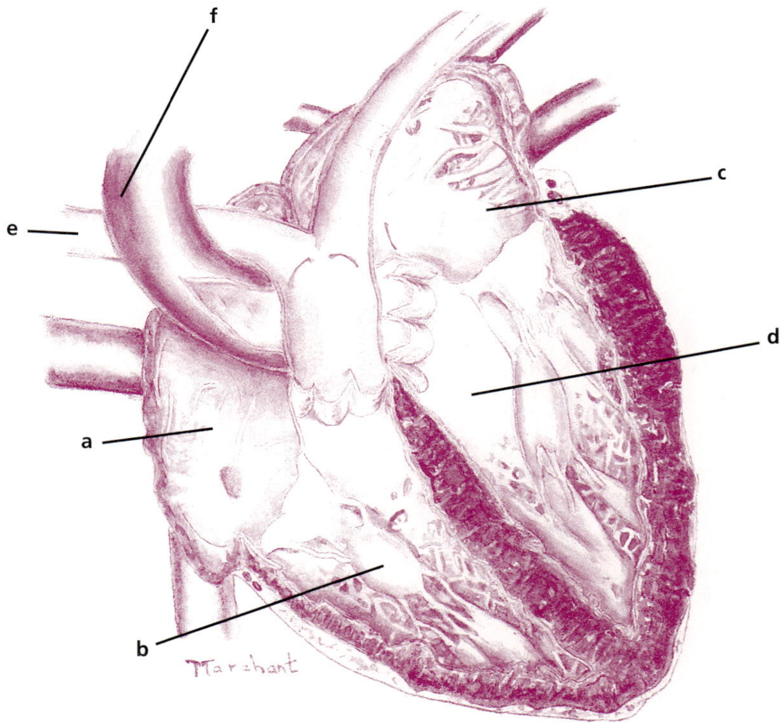

Fig. 5-3 *The heart.*

60 Name the structures of the respiratory system indicated in Figure 5-4.

a ______________________

b ______________________

c ______________________

d ______________________

e ______________________

f ______________________

g ______________________

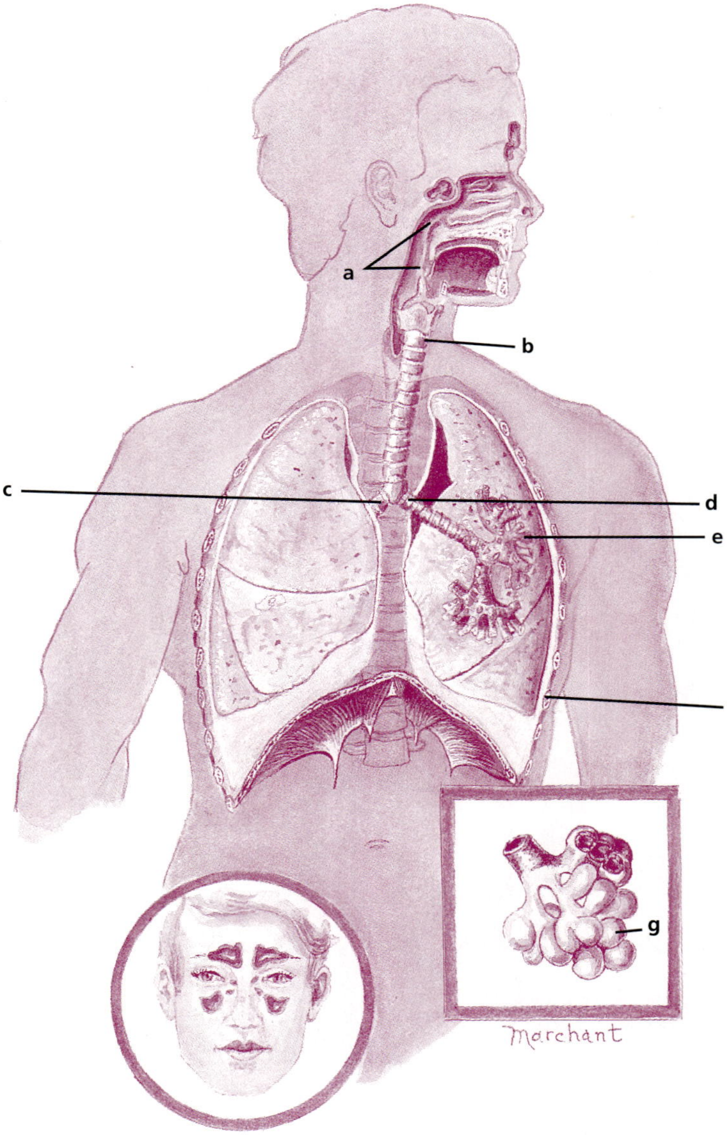

Fig. 5-4 *The respiratory system.*

61 Name the structures of the digestive system indicated in Figure 5-5.

a ______________________________

b ______________________________

c ______________________________

d ______________________________

e ______________________________

f ______________________________

g ______________________________

h ______________________________

i ______________________________

j ______________________________

k ______________________________

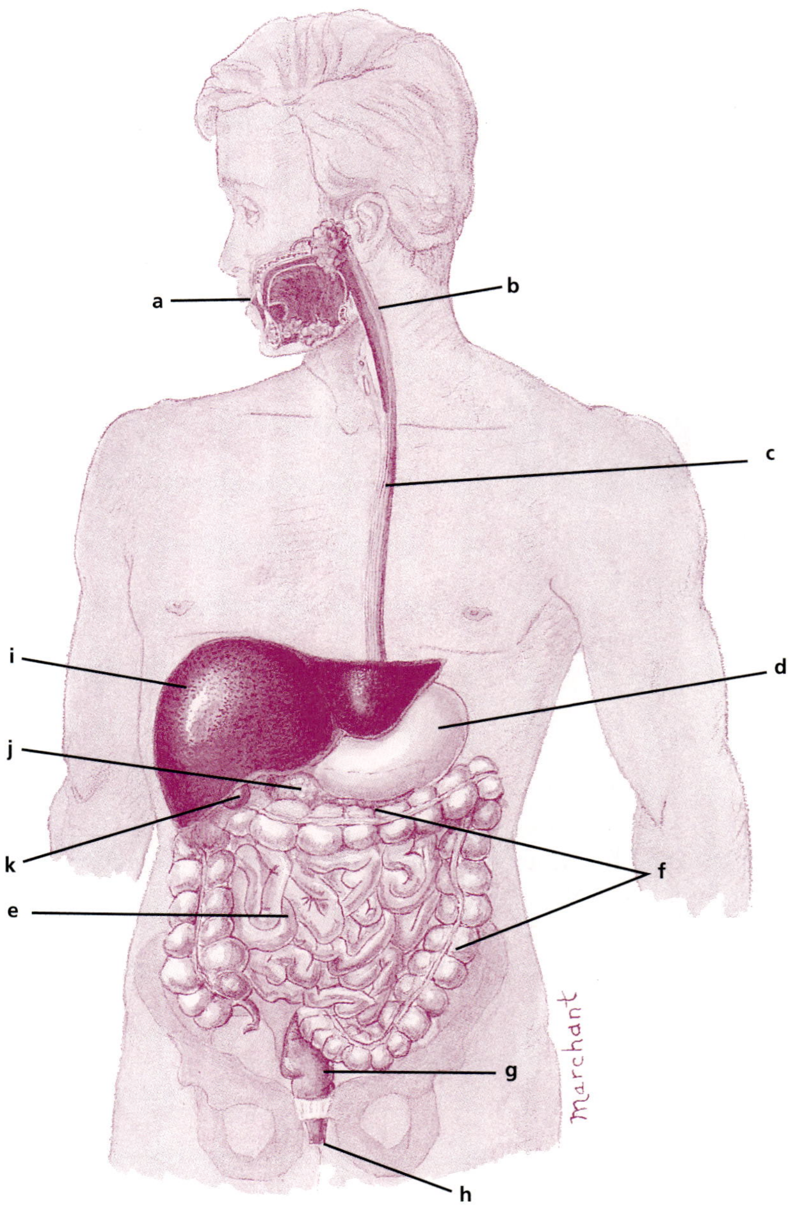

Fig. 5-5 *The digestive system.*

62 Name the structures of the urinary system indicated in Figure 5-6.

a ______________________________

b ______________________________

c ______________________________

d ______________________________

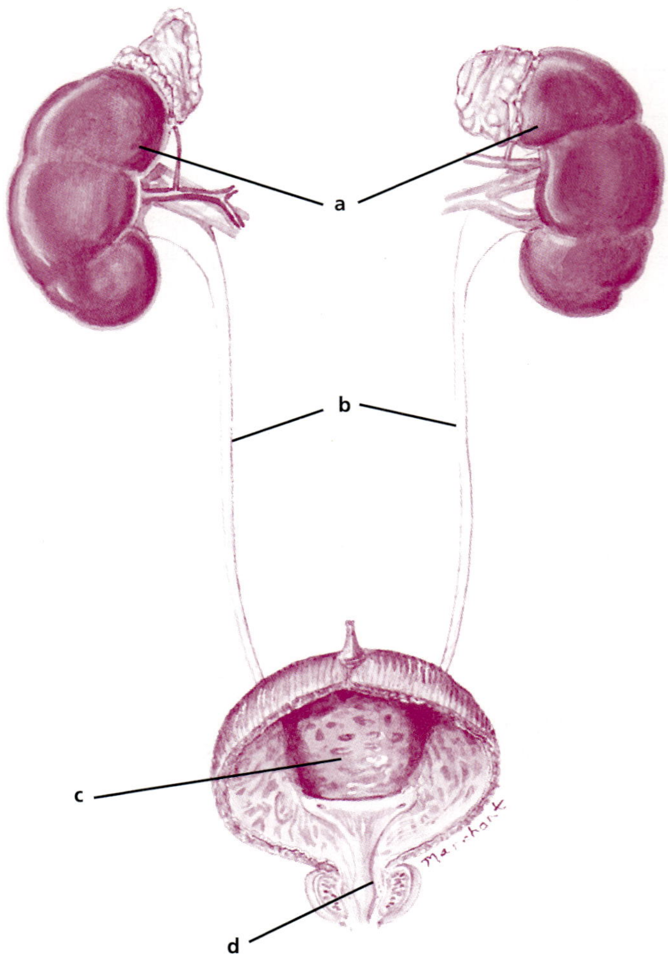

Fig. 5-6 *The urinary system.*

63 Name the structure and functions of the parts of the male reproductive system indicated in Figure 5-7.

a ______________________________

____

b ______________________________

____

c ______________________________

____

d ____

____

e ____

____

f ____

____

g ____

____

h ____

____

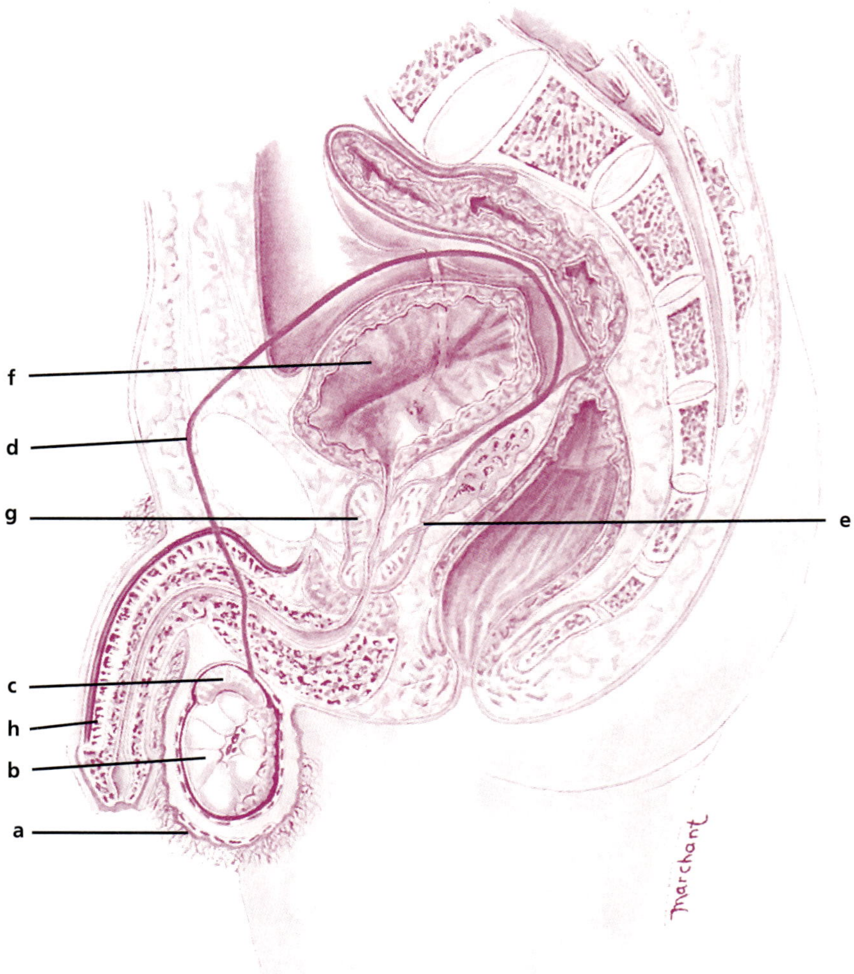

Fig. 5-7 *The male reproductive system.*

64 Name the structures of the external female genitalia as indicated in Figure 5-8.

a ______________________________

b ______________________________

c ______________________________

d ______________________________

e ______________________________

f ______________________________

g ______________________________

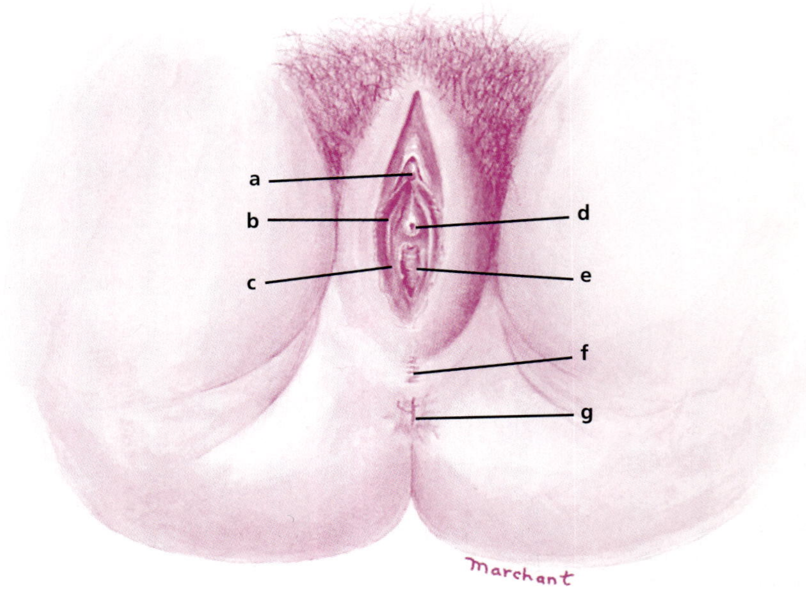

Fig. 5-8 *The external female genitalia.*

6

Growth and Development

PERSONAL EXPLORATIONS

1 Observe or interview one person in three or four of the age groups discussed in Chapter 6 of the textbook. (For example, you may want to observe three or four children in different age groups, or two children and two adults in different age groups.) Find out how the person has met or is working toward meeting the developmental tasks for each group.

2 Choose an age group between infancy and adolescence. Observe two or more children in the group. Compare how children of about the same age are meeting the developmental tasks. What differences or similarities are observed?

CAREER PREPARATIONS

Fill-in-the-Blanks

Fill in the word or phrase that best completes the sentence or answers the question. According to your textbook, at what age is a child expected to develop each of the following skills?

1 ______ Speaks in short sentences

2 ______ Usually protective of younger brothers and sisters

3 ______ Learns to write rather than print

4 ______ Smiles and follows objects with the eyes

5 ______ Can eat table food

6 ______ Capable of bladder control during the day

7 ______ Can hold a rattle

8 ______ Knows male and female bodies are different

9 ______ Reacts to the word "no"

10 ______ Bragging and showing off are common

11 ______ Begins to bite and chew finger foods

12 ______ Plays with the toes

13 What are the six basic principles of growth and development?

a ______________________________

____

b ______________________________

____

c ______________________________

____

d ______________________________

____

e ______________________________

____

f ______________________________

____

14 Physical changes that can be measured and occur in a steady and organized manner are called ____________________.

15 A change in psychological and social functioning is called ____________________.

16 A ____________________ is a baby in the first 4 weeks after birth.

17 The 4-year-old child has a strong preference for the parent of the ____________________ sex.

18 At what age are peer group activities and opinions important to a child?

____

19 Adolescence begins when reproductive organs begin to function. What is this event called? ____________________

20 During ____________________ hobbies and pastimes can be pursued as more free time is available.

Matching

Match the following statements with the correct reflex of an infant.

a Moro (startle) reflex
b Rooting reflex
c Sucking reflex
d Grasping reflex

21 ______ It is produced by touching the cheek.

22 ______ When the cheek is touched, a baby turns its head in the direction of the touch.

23 ______ A loud noise causes the infant to throw arms apart and extend legs.

24 ______ When the palm of the hand is touched, the baby closes its fingers around object.

25 ______ It guides a baby's mouth to the nipple.

26 ______ It disappears by the third month.

Match the developmental task with the correct age group.

a Infancy (birth to 1 year)
b Toddler (1 to 3 years)
c Preschooler (3 to 6 years)
d Middle childhood (6 to 8 years)
e Late childhood (9 to 12 years)
f Adolescence (12 to 18 years)
g Young adulthood (18 to 40 years)
h Middle adulthood (40 to 65 years)
i Late adulthood (65 years and older)

27 ______ Accepting the changes in body and appearance

28 ______ Developing leisure-time activities

29 ______ Gaining control of bowel and bladder functions

30 ______ Becoming independent from parents and adults

31 ______ Learning to eat solid foods

32 ______ Developing new friends and relationships

33 ______ Learning how to study

34 ______ Learning to get along with peers

35 ______ Increasing ability to communicate and understand others

36 ______ Tolerating separation from primary caregiver

37 ______ Learning to live with a husband or wife

38 ______ Developing moral and ethical behavior

39 ______ Learning basic reading, writing, and arithmetic skills

40 ______ Developing stable sleep and feeding patterns

41 ______ Performing self-care activities

42 ______ Using words to communicate with others

43 ______ Relating to aging parents

44 ______ Accepting male or female role appropriate for one's age

45 ______ Beginning to have emotional relationships with primary caregivers, brothers, and sisters

Riddles

Read the statements and solve the riddle.

46 What am I? ____________________

During this stage, the developmental tasks include

- adjusting to physical changes;
- having grown children;
- developing leisure-time activities; and
- relating to aging parents.

47 What am I? ____________________

During this stage, the developmental tasks include

- increasing the ability to communicate and understand others;
- performing self-care activities;
- learning all the differences between the sexes and developing sexual modesty;
- learning right from wrong and good from bad;
- learning to play with others; and
- developing family relationships.

1 Care of the Elderly

PERSONAL EXPLORATIONS

1 Interview an elderly person who lives independently. What concerns does the person have about remaining independent? Use these suggestions to guide your conversation.

- What physical problems does the person have, if any?
- What ways does the person use to provide safety for himself/herself?
- What comfort measures are used to decrease pain or help the person sleep?
- How does the person get to the store for groceries and other needs?
- How are needs for socialization met?

2 Interview an elderly person about being young. Observe facial expressions and tone of voice when the person talks about events he/she remembers. What changes do you see from the usual appearance of the person? Compare how well the person remembers events of long ago with events that occurred recently. How do you feel about the person after hearing about the person's youth? Use these suggestions to guide your conversation.

- What did the person do for a living?
- Ask to see any pictures of the person from long ago.
- What stories about family and friends make the person happy? Sad?
- Ask about historical events the person remembers.

CAREER PREPARATIONS

Word Jumblers

Unscramble the terms and use the circled letters to make a word that completes the sentence.

1 a C A V Y I R P

_ ◯ _ _ _ _ _

b F I N O C N E D T A L I T I Y

_ _ _ _ _ ◯ ◯ _ _ _ _ _ _ _ _

c L A N S P E R O   C O I H C E

_ _ _ ◯ _ _ _ _   _ ◯ _ _ _ _

d R O N V I E N T E N M

_ _ _ ◯ _ _ _ _ _ ◯ _

e T A C V I T I E S

_ _ ◯ _ _ _ _ _ ◯

f L I Q U A T Y   F O   F I E L

_ _ _ _ ◯ _ _   _ _   _ _ _ ◯

g M E D O R E F   F M O R   N E L G T E C

_ ◯ _ _ _ _ _   _ _ _ _   _ _ ◯ _ _ _ ◯

h Nursing facilities protect

_ _ _ _ _ _ _ _ _   _ _ _ _ _ _

Matching

Match the effects of aging with the correct type of change.

a Physical
b Psychological
c Social

2 ______ Graying hair

3 ______ Preparing for one's own death

4 ______ Death of a spouse

5 ______ Slower movements

6 ______ Retirement

Match the statement about the aging process with the body system affected.

a Integumentary
b Musculoskeletal
c Nervous
d Cardiovascular
e Respiratory
f Digestive
g Urinary

7 ______ Decreasing strength and mobility

8 ______ Changing sleeping patterns

9 ______ Less blood flowing through narrowed arteries

10 ______ Folds, lines, and wrinkles appearing

11 ______ Lung tissue becoming less elastic

12 ______ Decreased appetite and increased indigestion

13 ______ Poisonous substances building up in blood

14 ______ Increased sensitivity to cold

15 ______ Reduced sense of touch

16 ______ Urinary frequency and urgency occurring

Match the living arrangements or care methods with the advantage(s) of that arrangement.

a Living with family
b Respite care
c Adult day care centers
d Apartment
e Residential hotels
f Senior citizen housing
g Independent living units
h Hospital long-term care unit

17 ______ Food service or help is nearby for the elderly who are taking care of themselves.

18 ______ It provides activities for elderly person who cannot be left alone all day.

19 ______ It allows a caregiver to take a vacation or a rest.

20 ______ Elderly relatives provide companionship and share living expenses.

21 ______ Yard work, snow removal, or major repairs are the landlord's responsibility.

22 ______ Private rooms or efficiency apartments and food services are available in same building.

23 ______ Elderly persons or couples live independently in apartments near people of the same age.

24 ______ It gives care to person between an acute care unit and home or a nursing home.

Fill-in-the-Blanks

Fill in the word or phrase that best completes the sentence or answers the question.

25 What are two common causes of loneliness in the elderly?

a ______________________________

b ______________________________

26 Why are there usually more widows than widowers?

____

27 Elderly people often complain of feeling cold. What are some ways you can safely provide warmth?

a ______________________________

b ______________________________

c ______________________________

28 How can loss of bone and muscle strength be slowed?

a ______________________________

b ______________________________

29 Elderly persons who are mentally active and involved in current events show fewer ______________ and ______________ changes.

30 What body system will be affected by the care measures described?

a Performing range-of-motion exercises

____

b Providing a sweater and a lap blanket for a person who is cold

____

c Explaining to a person what you are going to do and why

____

d Placing the person in a semi-Fowler's position

____

31 What body systems function better with a moderate amount of daily exercise?

a ______________ **c** ______________

b ______________ **d** ______________

32 A person who has trouble breathing will find it easier to breathe if the bed is in a ______________ position.

33 If you suspect abuse of an elderly person, you should report this to the ______________.

34 What type of abuse is described in each of the following statements?

a This type of abuse involves hitting, slapping, kicking, pinching, and beating.

____

b This type of abuse is described as the use of oral or written words or statements that speak badly of, sneer at, criticize, or condemn the person.

____

c In this type of abuse the person is confined to a specific area.

____

d In this type of abuse, the person is humiliated and threatened with being punished or deprived of things.

____

Which Resident Right under the OBRA Requirements is described in these statements?

35 _______________ The person should be informed about care in a language that he/she understands.

36 _______________ A person who does not give consent cannot be treated.

37 _______________ The person is asked whether a student may observe a procedure.

38 _______________ The person chooses his/her clothes each day.

39 _______________ Two residents have a disagreement and ask the nurse to help with a settlement.

40 _______________ The resident is allowed to help with planting a garden.

41 _______________ Families are invited to participate in meetings at the facility.

42 _______________ The nursing assistant asks permission before looking through a person's dresser drawers.

43 _______________ A nursing assistant is fired because he/she slapped a resident.

44 _______________ The physician must write an order for restraints to be used.

45 _______________ The nursing assistant is always polite and courteous when talking to a resident.

46 _______________ Religious services are held regularly for residents.

47 _______________ The residence home is decorated so that it looks like a private home rather than a hospital.

What are the forms of abuse described in these statements?

48 ______________________ A person is deprived of needed medical care.

49 ______________________ A resident is teased and made fun of by an employee.

50 ______________________ An elderly person is locked in his/her room.

51 ______________________ A son spends his mother's pension check without her permission.

52 ______________________ Threats are made to an elderly person that say the person will be deprived of food or shelter.

53 ______________________ An elderly person is forced to perform sexual acts.

54 Should an elderly person increase or decrease these dietary elements? Why?

- **a** Calories ______________________ Why? ______________________
- **b** Fluids ______________________ Why? ______________________
- **c** Protein ______________________ Why? ______________________
- **d** Soft bulk ______________________ Why? ______________________

55 Why should you make sure an elderly person reduces fluid intake after 5 PM?

____

Choose the Correct Answer

Circle the letter next to the statement that best completes the sentence or answers the question.

56 Which of the following physical changes is most likely to cause confusion or behavioral changes in an elderly person?

- **a** Respiratory infections
- **b** Lack of exercise
- **c** Blood flow to brain is reduced
- **d** Poor fluid intake

57 Why does an elderly person usually require a bath only twice a week?

- **a** Less exercise is done so frequent bathing is unnecessary.
- **b** Fewer baths decrease the possibility of injury from falls in the tub.
- **c** Skin becomes drier with aging and is easily damaged by frequent bathing.
- **d** Muscles atrophy and strength is reduced.

58 Why should you avoid applying heat to the feet of an elderly person?

- **a** The skin is dry and has decreased oil glands.
- **b** More fold lines and wrinkles appear in the skin.
- **c** The feet may become infected more easily.
- **d** Decreased sensitivity to heat may increase risk of burns.

8 Safety

PERSONAL EXPLORATIONS

1 Safety is important to everyone and needs to be practiced all the time. Check these items or areas in your own home to determine how safe your home is.

- What areas have adequate lighting for safety? How can the lighting be improved?
- Check the electrical cords and plugs on appliances and lamps. How many did you discover that were frayed and damaged? What can you do to correct the unsafe cords or plugs?
- Do you have a working smoke detector in your home? When were the batteries last changed? How often should batteries be replaced?
- How many throw rugs are being used on slippery surfaces? Do they have non-skid backing?
- Where are medicines or household cleansers kept in your home? If they are within the reach of children, where could they be placed to be out of the reach of children?
- Make a list of the good safety practices you found in your home. Make another list of safety practices that could be improved.

2 Develop a plan for your home and family that helps everyone to escape if a fire occurs.

- Make sure each person knows at least two escape routes from the sleeping area.
- Practice how to check a door for heat before opening it.
- Arrange a place to meet once you are outside of the building.

3 Role play this situation about a person who is restrained. Take turns being the nursing assistant and the person being restrained. In order to feel as the person feels, you should be left alone for the full 20 minutes of the role play. Use the questions to think about how you felt when you were restrained. You may think of other observations to add. After you have completed the role play, talk with your classmate and discuss how this situation helped to identify changes you will make when you need to restrain a person in the future.

SITUATION: Ms. Martha Whitacre, 92, resides in a nursing home. She is alert and oriented, but she has fallen several times when she gets up without help. The nurse tells the nursing assistant that Martha needs to have a vest restraint on to keep her from falling. The nursing assistant applies the restraint and settles Martha in the TV room. Twenty minutes have gone by and no one is around.

Now, consider these questions about how you felt when you were "Ms. Whitacre."

- How did you feel when the nursing assistant said you had to be restrained?
- What did the nursing assistant say to you when the restraint was applied? Did you understand the need for the restraint?
- How did the restraint feel on your body?
- If you had been thirsty, how would you have gotten a drink?
- How comfortable was the chair? Was the chair padded? Were you able to reposition yourself if you had become tired sitting in one position?
- Were you asked if you needed to use the bathroom before the restraint was applied? How would you have gotten to the bathroom?
- How could you call for help? Was there a call bell in the TV room?
- Why were you in the TV room? Who decided that you would sit there? Who had control of the TV?

CAREER PREPARATIONS

Word Scramble

Unscramble these words to replace the underlined phrase in each sentence.

1 When Kevin was injured in a motorcycle accident, he suffered from paralysis from the waist down.

apiarapgle _ _ _ _ _ _ _ _ _ _

2 Charles suffered a stroke and has paralysis on the left side of his body.

peglaiimeh _ _ _ _ _ _ _ _ _ _

3 Carolyn is in a state of being completely unaware of her surroundings due to a head injury.

oacm _ _ _ _

4 When Cleon hit his head on a rock while diving, he developed paralysis from the neck down.

piluaqdgeria _ _ _ _ _ _ _ _ _ _ _ _

5 A sudden catastrophic event occurred and staff evacuated all of the patients/residents.

stadseir _ _ _ _ _ _ _ _

6 A smoky fire caused a baby to die from a termination of breathing that results from lack of oxygen.

fouscatfni _ _ _ _ _ _ _ _ _ _ _

Matching

Match the description or example with the correct restraint.

a Active physical restraint
b Chemical restraint
c Vest restraint
d Passive physical restraint
e Geriatric chair
f Mitt restraint
g Wrist restraint

7 ______ A drug is given that is not required to treat the person's medical symptoms.

8 ______ An attached tray keeps the person from getting up.

9 ______ Hands are covered to prevent the person from removing a dressing.

10 ______ If this is applied incorrectly, the person can strangle or suffocate.

11 ______ With this restraint, skin and circulation should be checked every 2 hours.

12 ______ This type of restraint attaches a person's body to a nonmovable object.

13 ______ This restraint does not restrict freedom and allows access to certain body parts.

Fill-in-the-Blanks

Fill in the word or phrase that best completes the sentence or answers the question.

14 What normal activities of young children put them at risk for injury?

a ______________________________

b ______________________________

c ______________________________

15 How do these physical changes in the elderly place them at risk for accidents?

a Movements are slower and less steady ______________________________

____

b Decreased sensitivity to heat and cold ______________________________

____

c Decreased sense of smell ______________________________

____

16 Why should you avoid calling a person by name as a method of identifying the person?

____

____

17 How do you help to prevent falls when you answer a call bell quickly?

____

____

18 If a person has signed a release to avoid having siderails used, the rails are still used whenever ____.

19 When a person is restrained, what should be done at least every 2 hours?

a ____

b ____

c ____

d ____

e ____

f ____

Choose the Correct Answer

Circle the letter next to the statement that best completes the sentence or answers the question.

20 Which of the following statements about the use of restraints is incorrect? (Circle *all* incorrect statements.)

a Unnecessary restraint is false imprisonment.
b Persons who are confused usually become calmer after being restrained.
c Using restraints for as little time as possible improves quality of life.
d You may apply restraints in a manner slightly different than the directions indicate, if needed.
e Restraints are used to protect the person.
f The least restrictive method must be used.
g Restraints may need to be applied rapidly.
h You should check the restrained person every hour to see if the person needs anything.
i Restraints are used before other methods are used to control the person.
j The nurse decides who needs to be restrained.
k Restraints may be used on a confused person without permission.

21 If a fire occurs, which of these steps should be done first?

a Use a fire extinguisher to put out the fire.
b Close all doors and windows.
c Sound the nearest fire alarm.
d Move persons who are in danger to a safe place.

22 Suffocation can occur because (circle ***all*** correct answers).

a a person chokes on a piece of food.
b a person is left unattended in a bathtub.
c restraints are applied correctly.
d a liquid is added to a feeding tube incorrectly.
e a person's dentures are loose.

23 If you discover a person has no pulse in a hand that is restrained, the first thing you should do is

a call the nurse.
b massage the hand.
c cut off the restraint.
d reposition the person.

24 When an accident occurs, it is correct to

a report the accident immediately to your supervisor.
b report the incident only if a person is injured.
c call the family immediately.
d call the doctor or ambulance.

True or False

Read each statement and circle T if it is true, F if it is false. If the statement is false, in the space beneath the statement, change the words to make the statement true.

25 T F One way to prevent poisoning of children is to make sure you store poisonous materials in the back of the cupboard.

____

26 T F A vest restraint may be applied so that it crosses either in the front or the back.

____

27 T F Elbow restraints are used on young children to prevent them from scratching or touching incisions.

____

28 T F If an electric plug is not grounded, it will cause a fire.

____

29 T F Visitors need to be reminded not to smoke in a room with supplemental oxygen, even if the facility has a "No Smoking" policy.

____

30 T F When supplemental oxygen is being used, visitors in the room may smoke a pipe.

____

31 T F Electrical equipment must be turned off before unplugging to prevent sparks.

____

32 T F Confused, disoriented, or sedated persons are never allowed to smoke.

____

33 T F You should attempt to put out a fire before sounding a fire alarm.

____

34 T F All fire extinguishers are effective for any fire.

____

Diagrams

35 **a** On Figure 8-1, identify the part of the body experiencing hemiplegia.

b On Figure 8-2, identify the part of the body experiencing paraplegia.

c On Figure 8-3, identify the part of the body experiencing quadriplegia.

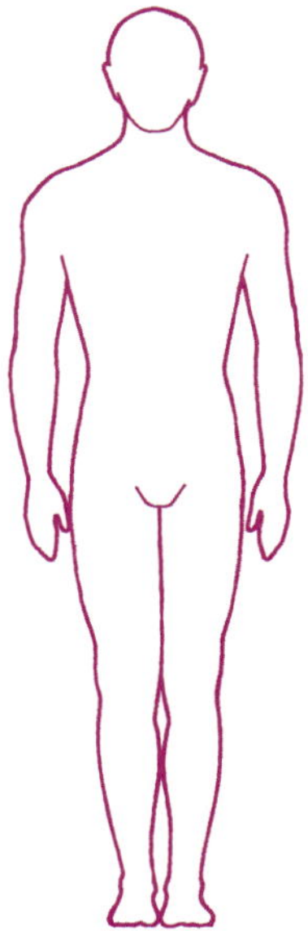

Fig. 8-1 *Hemiplegia.*

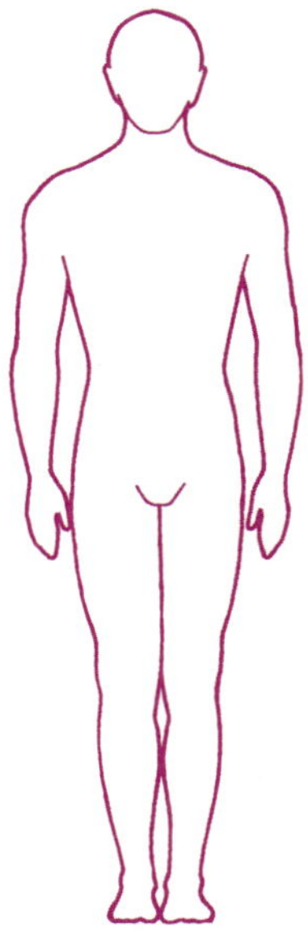

Fig. 8-2 *Paraplegia.*

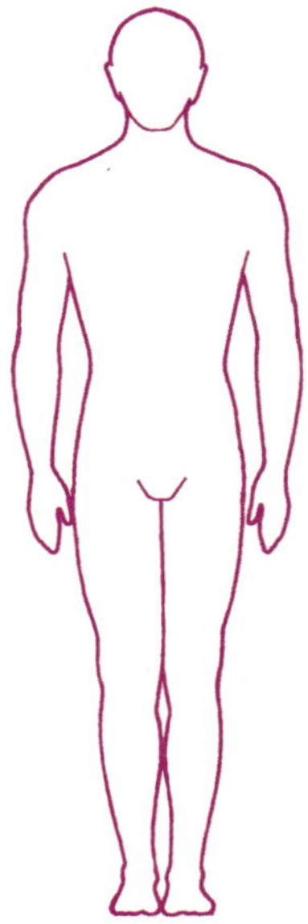

Fig. 8-3 *Quadriplegia.*

36 What are three safety measures that need to be taken for a person with each of the conditions in question 35?

a Hemiplegia

____

____

____

b Paraplegia

____

____

____

c Quadriplegia

____

____

____

9 Preventing Infection

PERSONAL EXPLORATIONS

1 Hand washing is an important practice to prevent the spread of infection. Make a list for one day (away from school or work) of the times and places you wash your hands. At the end of the day make a second list of times you should have washed your hands and did not. How can you improve your hand washing practice? How have your hand washing habits changed since studying this chapter? Did you use the hand washing procedure shown in Chapter 9 of the textbook during your daily life?

2 When you are working in a health care facility, you need to prevent the spread of infection. Use the situation to identify ways to prevent spreading disease.

Consider how you would answer these questions about caring for Mr. Gonzalez.

SITUATION: Jose Gonzalez, 50, is admitted to the hospital. He is in blood and body fluid isolation.

- What are the body fluids you are going to handle carefully?
- How can you protect yourself against infection in this situation? What will you wear?
- How will you dispose of vomitus? Stool? Urine? Respiratory secretions?
- How will you handle soiled tissues lying on the floor?

- What items will need to be labeled "Biohazard" when being removed from the room?
- What would you do if Mr. Gonzalez cut himself while shaving?
- What would you do if you cut your leg on the bed while working in his room?

CAREER PREPARATIONS

Crossword

Preventing Infection

ACROSS

5. Another name for a microorganism
6. Extremely small microorganisms that grow in living cells
7. Administration of a vaccine to produce immunity
9. Plants that live on other plants or animals
11. Disinfectant that can be applied to skin and tissue
13. Bacterium protected by a hard shell
14. Preparation containing microorganisms

DOWN

1. Absence of pathogens
2. Small living plant or animal that cannot be seen without a microscope
3. Communicable
4. Process by which pathogens are destroyed
8. Infection acquired after admission to a health care facility
10. One-celled microscopic animals
12. Environment in which microorganisms live and grow

Riddle

Read the statements and solve the riddle.

1 What are we? ______________________________

- We exist in five different forms.
- We can live in a person, a plant, an animal, soil, food, water, or other material.
- Some of us need oxygen; others do not.
- We all need a warm, dark environment to live and may be destroyed by heat and light.

Fill-in-the-Blanks

Fill in the word or phrase that best completes the sentence or answers the question.

2 *E. coli* is normal flora in the intestine. What happens if it enters the urinary tract? ______________________________

3 Why do you hold your hands down throughout the hand washing procedure?

____

4 Why do you turn off the water by using a paper towel to touch the hand-operated faucets? ______________________________

5 If you are wearing a gown and it becomes wet, what should you do and why?

____

6 Nosocomial infections are acquired

______________________________.

7 What are the most common sites for nosocomial infections?

a ______________ **c** ______________

b ______________ **d** ______________

8 The easiest and most important way to prevent infection is

______________________________.

Labeling

9 Label Figure 9-1, the chain of infection. Identify the components of the chain of infection and give an example of each component.

a ______________________

b ______________________

c ______________________

d ______________________

e ______________________

f ______________________

g ______________________

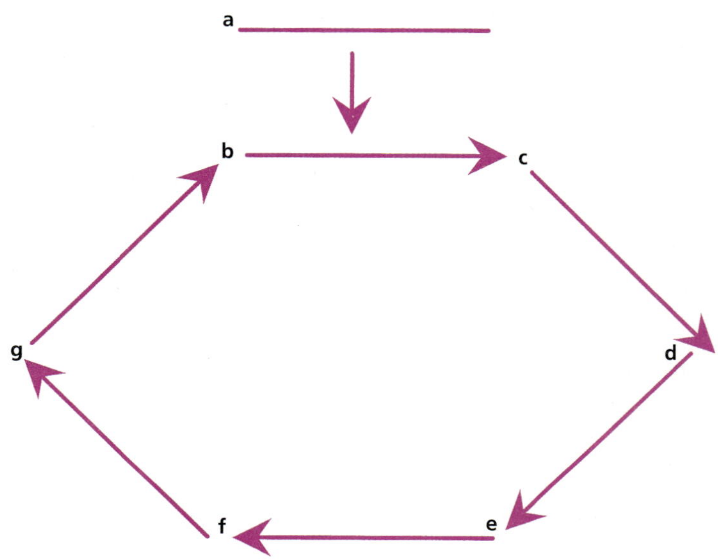

Fig. 9-1 *Chain of infection.*

Choose the Correct Answer

Circle the letter next to the statement that best completes the sentence or answers the question.

10 If the infection precautions include "Masks are worn by everyone having direct contact with the person," the type of precaution is

a blood/body fluid.
b strict.
c contact.
d acid-fast bacillus (AFB).

11 When you begin your shift in a health care facility, it would be a good practice to wash your hands for

a 3 to 5 minutes.
b 2 minutes.
c 10 to 15 seconds.
d 1 minute.

12 Which of these statements is **not** a good aseptic measure?

a Clean, unused equipment should not be taken from one person's room to another room.
b Clean from the dirtiest area to the cleanest.
c Wear protective equipment as needed.
d Keep tables and other surfaces clean and dry.

13 Here is a list of common aseptic practices that you should use. Which one is the most important to prevent the spread of infection?

a Bathing, washing hair, and brushing teeth regularly
b Washing cooking utensils with soap and water
c Disposing of garbage
d Covering nose and mouth when coughing or sneezing
e Washing hands after toileting or before eating
f Washing fruits and vegetables before eating
g Providing separate washcloths and towels for each person

14 Universal precautions should be used

a only when you think a person has an infection.
b only when you are changing soiled linens.
c only when you have open skin wounds.
d when caring for all people at all times.

15 When you are removing gloves after giving care, which part is considered "clean"?

a The inside
b The outside
c Both sides
d Neither side

16 The Bloodborne Pathogen Standard is primarily intended to protect workers from exposure to

a acid-fast bacillus.
b *E. coli.*
c HIV and HBV.
d protozoa and fungi.

17 Under Bloodborne Pathogen Standards, training about controlling exposure to these infections must be given to employees

a when the person is hired.
b every year.
c when new procedures are added.
d when procedures change.
e All of the above

18 A hepatitis B vaccination protects the person receiving it against a disease that affects the

a liver.
b blood.
c immune system.
d urinary system.

19 If a container is labeled "Biohazard," it contains materials that are

a sterile.
b clean.
c contaminated.
d poisonous.

20 Which, if any, of these gloves can be reused after cleaning?

a Sterile gloves
b Disposable gloves
c Utility gloves
d None of the above

Diagram

21 In Figure 9-2, identify the parts of the hands that are frequently missed during hand washing.

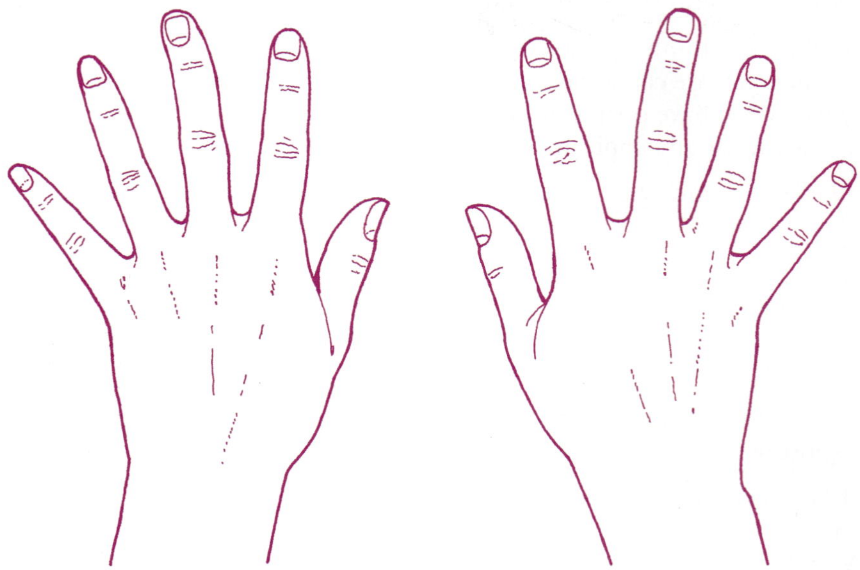

Fig. 9-2 *Hand washing.*

22 In Figure 9-3, identify the part of the mask that is considered contaminated after use.

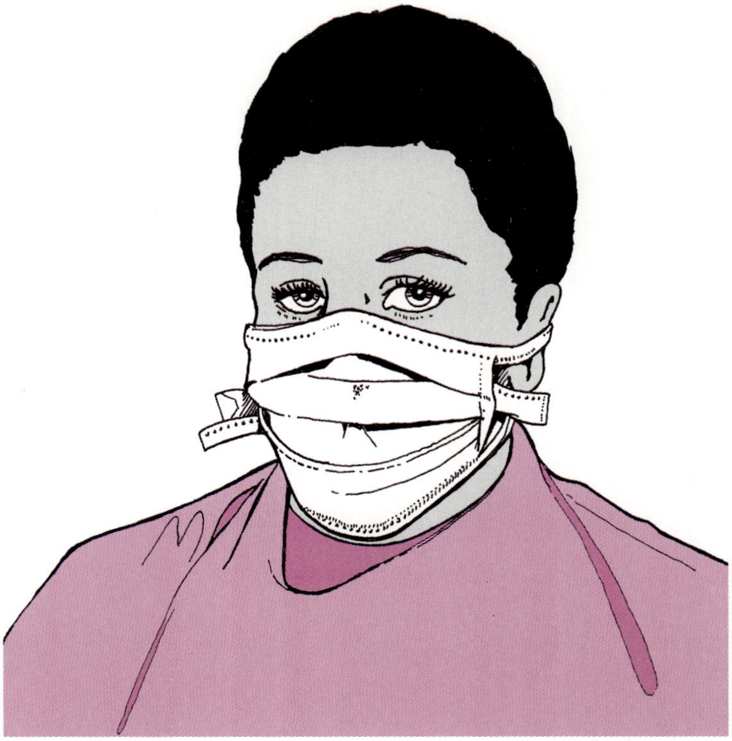

Fig. 9-3 *Mask.*

23 In Figure 9-4, identify the part of the gown that is considered contaminated after use.

Fig. 9-4 *Gown.*

10 Body Mechanics

PERSONAL EXPLORATIONS

1 For one day, pay attention to how well you use body mechanics in your daily life. When did you use correct methods to prevent strain or injury? When could you have used better body mechanics?

Consider if you had performed the following actions:

- Lifting school books by bending your knees rather than bending your back;
- Carrying trash to the garbage can holding it close to your body;
- Carrying groceries into the house holding the bags close to your body; or
- Making two or more trips when carrying items rather than trying to carry too much at once.

2 Role play this situation with a classmate. Take turns acting as the nursing assistant and the person being positioned. Have a third classmate act as an observer to tell each of you when you used good body mechanics and when you did not.

SITUATION: Roger Green, 78, had a CVA (stroke) last month. He has hemiplegia on his right side. The nurse asks you to turn him from his back to his left side and position him comfortably.

Consider these questions about the positioning of a person.

- How can you turn Mr. Green to prevent injury to him?
- What assisting devices could you use? How would they be helpful?
- How many pillows are needed for comfort and good alignment?
- When you are playing Mr. Green, how does it feel to be moved by someone else?
- After you are positioned, are you comfortable?

3 Role play this situation with two classmates. Take turns acting as the nursing assistant and the person being transferred. Be sure you do not place weight on your right leg when you are Ms. Simpson.

SITUATION: Myra Simpson, 52, fell while jogging and injured her right leg. She needs to be transported by wheelchair to the radiology department. You are assigned to get her ready to go. Consider these questions to determine how you will safely move Ms. Simpson.

- How will you prepare Ms. Simpson for the transfer? What will you tell her? What clothing should she wear?
- How will you prepare the wheelchair? Safety preparation? Comfort concerns?
- On which side of the bed will you position the wheelchair? Why?
- What assessments of Ms. Simpson are likely to be done before and after the transfer? Why?
- What factors would determine whether you will use a transfer belt or not?
- How will you position yourself as you prepare to transfer Ms. Simpson?
- How will you move to prevent injury to yourself?

CAREER PREPARATIONS

Word Search

Write the correct word next to each definition. Then circle or highlight the words in the puzzle.

A	B	O	D	Y	M	E	C	H	A	N	P	S	I	T	S
C	O	J	D	E	O	L	S	L	A	T	E	R	A	L	P
Z	Y	E	R	A	O	Q	T	O	D	D	R	A	O	O	R
L	F	R	A	R	W	U	M	G	N	T	A	I	T	N	I
O	R	O	W	S	H	E	A	R	I	N	G	N	H	O	E
L	I	T	S	Z	I	S	T	O	M	G	A	K	G	A	L
T	C	A	H	Y	U	M	O	L	V	T	I	L	O	L	M
S	T	E	E	P	L	T	S	L	O	A	T	E	A	I	E
O	I	L	E	S	R	Y	V	I	O	N	B	I	N	G	L
P	O	S	T	U	R	E	S	N	N	W	E	B	A	N	T
O	N	T	O	P	O	F	T	G	E	T	L	V	O	M	Z
P	F	O	L	I	N	O	L	I	R	X	T	M	E	E	T
U	R	R	O	N	C	F	O	W	L	E	R	S	O	N	P
P	Y	W	H	E	E	L	C	H	A	I	R	B	O	T	E

1. ______________ Rubbing of one surface against another
2. ______________ Way in which body parts are aligned with one another
3. ______________ When the skin sticks to a surface and the muscles slide in the direction the body is moving
4. ______________ Transfer belt
5. ______________ Turning the person as a unit in alignment in one motion
6. ______________ Backlying or dorsal recumbent position
7. ______________ Sidelying position
8. ______________ Semisitting position with the head of the bed elevated 45° to 60°
9. ______________ Sidelying position in which upper leg is sharply flexed
10. ______________ Another word for posture
11. ______________ A lift sheet; a turn or pull sheet
12. ______________ Sit on the edge of the bed
13. ______________ Position on abdomen with head turned to one side
14. ______________ Chair used to move a person from one place to another

Fill-in-the-Blanks

Fill in the word or phrase that best completes the sentence or answers the question.

15 How can you provide a better base of support for yourself when lifting?

____

16 When you move a person up in bed, it is important to protect the skin from

______________________________.

17 In the procedures in this chapter, the first six steps are often the same. Explain why each one is important.

a Ask a co-worker for help. ______________________________

____

b Wash your hands. ______________________________

____

c Identify the person. ______________________________

____

d Explain what you are going to do. ______________________________

____

e Provide for privacy. ______________________________

____

f Lock the bed wheels. ______________________________

____

18 When moving a person up in bed, why should you place the pillow against the headboard?

____

19 Why should the level of the bed be raised when the person is being repositioned?

____

20 When you are assisting a co-worker or asking a person to help with moving another person up in bed, why do you count to "3"?

____

21 Why is logrolling used to move the person?

____

22 What observations should you make when the person is dangling?

a ______________________________

b ______________________________

c ______________________________

d ______________________________

e ______________________________

f ______________________________

23 Why should you get a person up on his/her strong side?

____

24 Why do you pad the seat of the wheelchair?

____

25 How often should a person be repositioned when lying in bed or sitting in a chair? _______________

Labeling

Identify and label the five basic positions illustrated.

26 In Figure 10-1, the position is _______________.

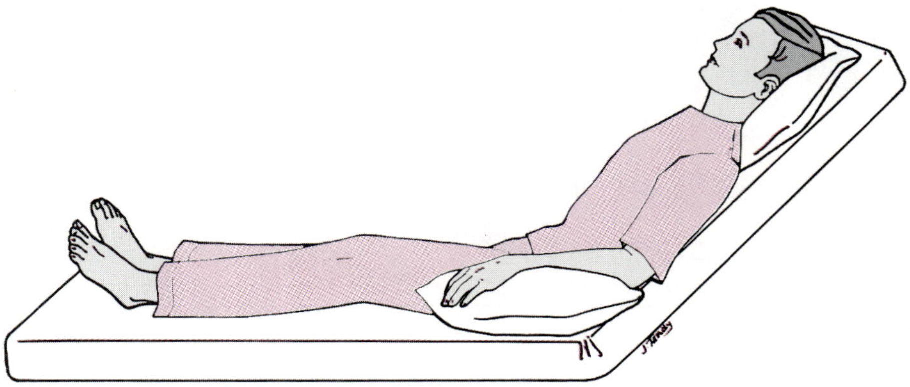

Fig. 10-1

27 In Figure 10-2, the position is _______________.

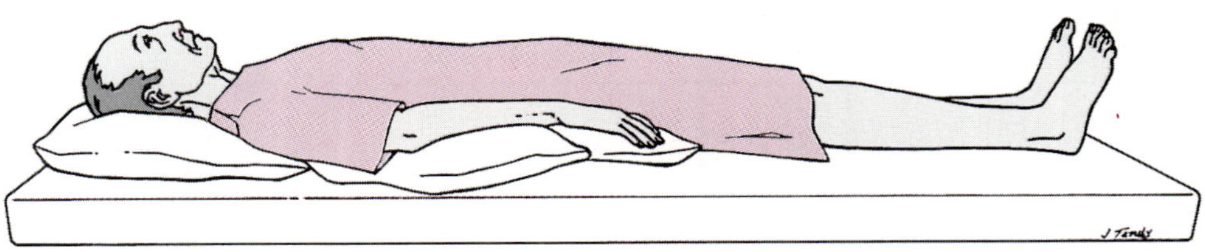

Fig. 10-2

28 In Figure 10-3, the position is _______________.

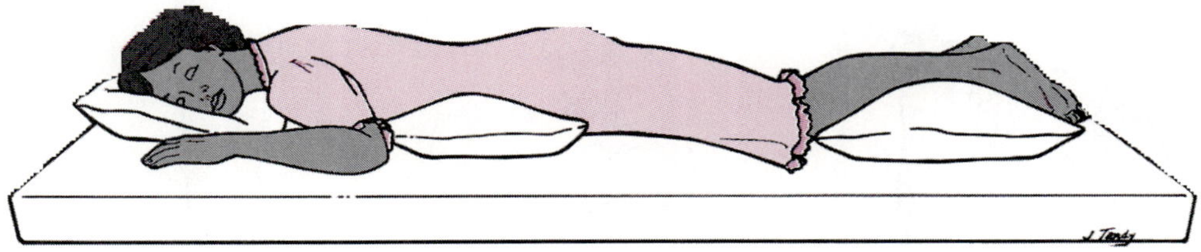

Fig. 10-3

29 In Figure 10-4, the position is ______________________________.

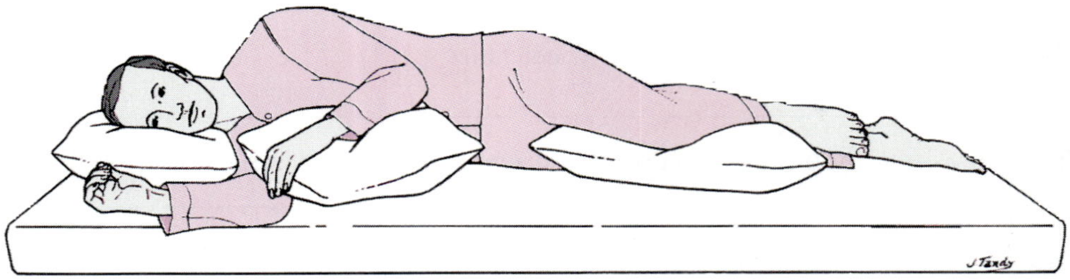

Fig. 10-4

30 In Figure 10-5, the position is ______________________________.

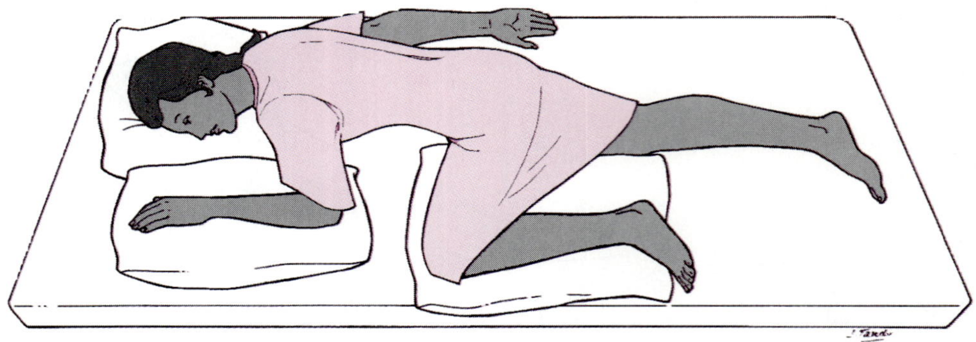

Fig. 10-5

31 Which of the drawings in Figure 10-6, A and B, shows the correct way to lift heavy objects?

____

32 When lifting correctly as shown in Figure 10-6, A and B, which muscles are used?

____

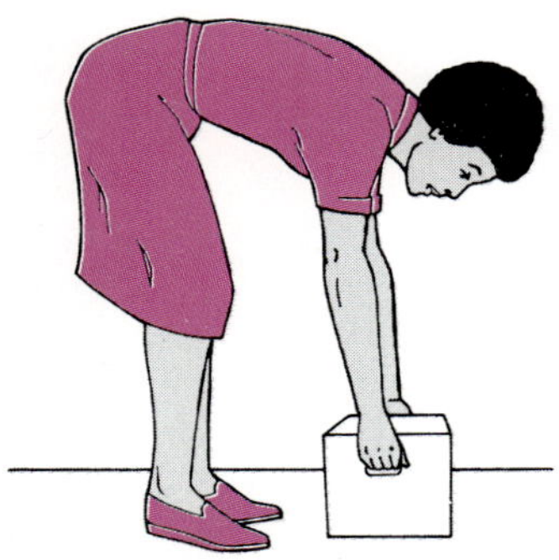

Fig. 10-6A

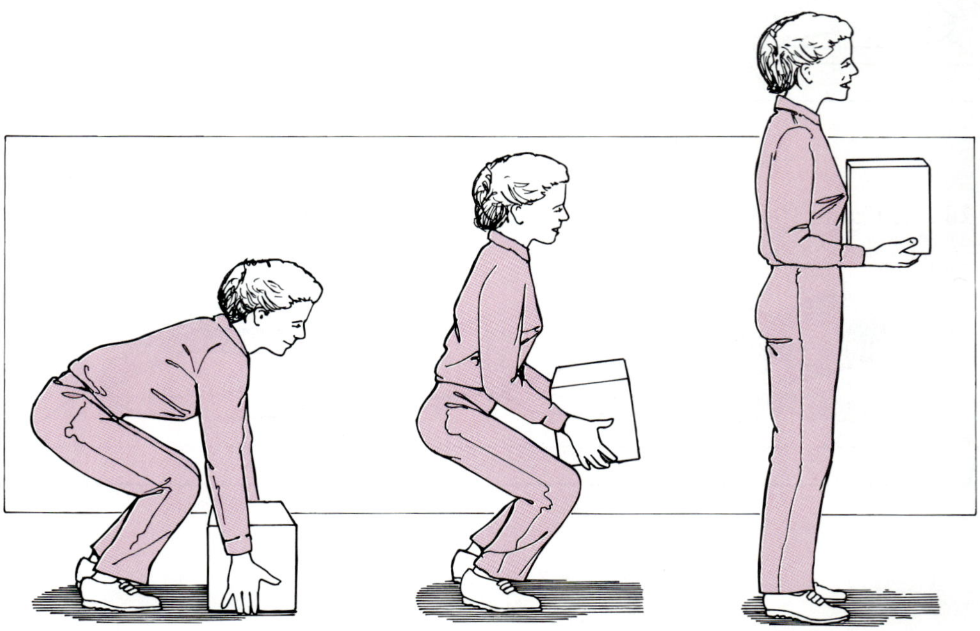

Fig. 10-6B

33 When lifting as shown in Figure 10-7, what parts of the body are used?

____

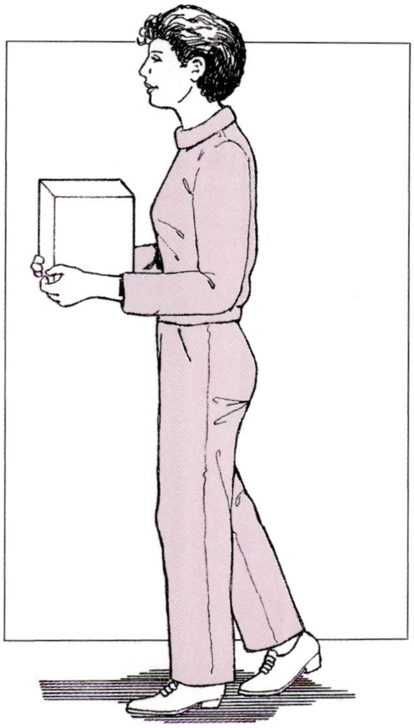

Fig. 10-7

34 The woman in Figure 10-8 has been positioned on her side. Identify where pillows should be properly placed. How many pillows did you draw?

____

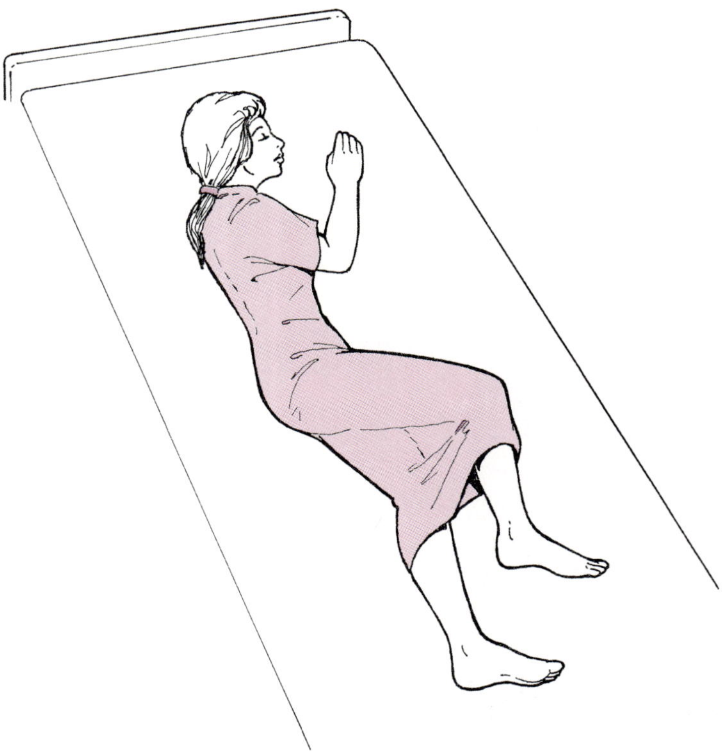

Fig. 10-8

11 The Patient/ Resident Unit

PERSONAL EXPLORATIONS

1 Find an empty patient room and practice using the equipment. Answer these questions about your practice.

- How do you operate the head of the bed? What do you do to adjust the height of the overbed table?
- How do you operate the knee control of the bed?
- How does the call light work?
- Where are the controls for the television and radio?

2 Answer these questions about how the staff knows when a person needs help.

- How does the staff know when a person turns on a call light?
- Is there only a light outside of the room or does a light come on somewhere else on the unit? If so, where?
- What sound does the signal make?
- If the person signals from the bathroom, is that signal light and sound the same or different from the signal at the bed? If it is different, what does it sound like?

3 Check the temperature in your home. People have different temperatures at which they are comfortable. Answer these questions about yourself to help you understand the importance of individual preferences for persons in a health care setting.

- Do you prefer hot/cold rooms? Why?
- How does the temperature that you prefer compare to that of your spouse, children, or friends?
- Would the temperature you prefer be appropriate for an infant? An elderly person? Why or why not?

4 How does noise in your home affect you? Answer these questions to help you understand the importance of noise levels in the health care facility.

- How do you study best? With the radio or TV playing? With silence?
- When you go to bed do you prefer silence to help you to sleep? Do you like soft music or the TV as you go to sleep?
- Does everyone in your household agree on how loudly or softly to play a radio or the TV? How do you resolve conflict over this, if it is a problem?
- If the noise level in your surroundings is unacceptable to you, how do you react? How does it affect your ability to think? Rest? Study? How does it affect your relationship with others?

CAREER PREPARATIONS

Fill-in-the-Blanks

Fill in the word or phrase that best completes the sentence or answers the question.

1 What factors that affect comfort for a person in a health care facility can be controlled by the nursing assistant?

a ____________________

b ____________________

c ____________________

d ____________________

e ____________________

Look at the factors affecting comfort that you identified in question 1. Write the factor being controlled by each of the following actions.

2 ______ Adjusting the thermostat in the room

3 ______ Turning lights down during rest periods

4 ______ Emptying bedpans and urinals promptly

5 ______ Washing hands after smoking

6 ______ Answering call lights and telephones quickly

7 ______ Making sure the person has good personal care

8 ______ Talking quietly to other staff members

9 ______ Opening shades or drapes when the person is reading

10 Higher room temperatures will probably be needed by

________________ and ________________.

11 What are the 4 basic bed positions described below?

a 45° sitting position ________________

b Head elevated 30° to 45°; knees may be raised 15°

____

c Head of bed down, foot up ________________

d Head of bed up, foot down ________________

12 The nursing team may use the overbed table as a work area, but should only place ________________ or ________________ items on the table.

13 What items are kept on the lower shelf of the bedside stand?

a ________________

b ________________

c ________________

14 Why are toilets in some facilities higher than standard toilets?

a ____

b ____

Choose the Correct Answer

Circle the letter next to the statement that best completes the sentence or answers the question.

15 The call light should *always* be

a on the bedrail.
b attached to the pillow.
c within the person's reach.
d on the arm of the chair.

16 If you wish to locate an item in a person's closet, you should

a wait until he/she is out of the room to search.
b tell him/her you must find the item and begin to search.
c ask his/her permission to look for the item.
d inform the nurse and have him/her look for the item.

17 When you carry out the correct action in question 16, you are following the OBRA requirement to provide

a a safe environment.
b personal choice.
c right to privacy.
d freedom from restraint.

Labeling

18 Explain the use of each handle on the manually operated bed in Figure 11-1.

a ______________________

b ______________________

c ______________________

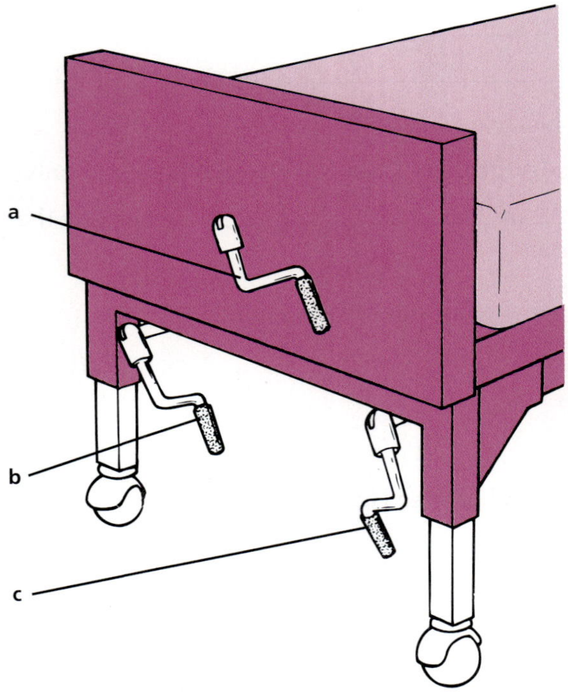

Fig. 11-1 *A manually operated bed.*

19 Explain the use of each lever on the electric bed shown in Figure 11-2.

a ______________________________

b ______________________________

c ______________________________

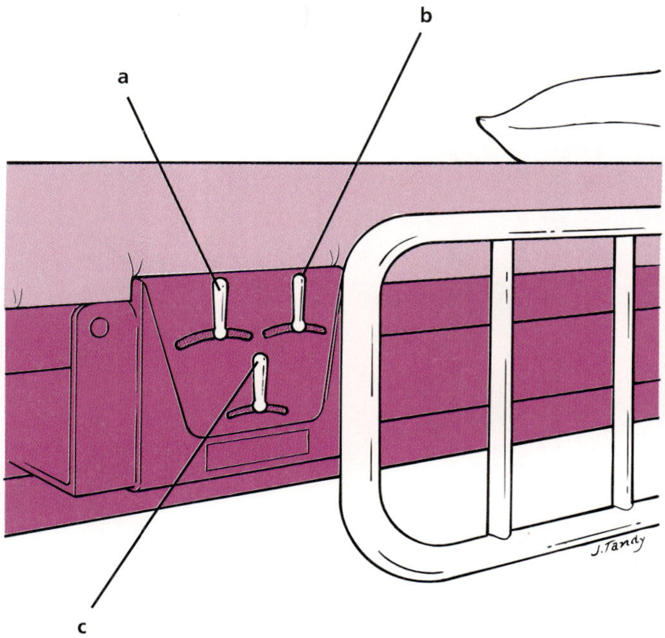

Fig. 11-2 *An electric bed.*

12 Bedmaking

PERSONAL EXPLORATIONS

1 When you make beds this week, follow the new methods you have learned. Use these statements as a guide. How did these new techniques change your bedmaking practices? How many steps did you save by being organized?

- Gather linens in the order they will be used.
- Remove old linens and carry them without touching them to your body.
- Make as much of one side of the bed as you can before moving to the opposite side.
- Make mitered corners when possible.
- Place pillows with opening facing away from the doorway.

2 Role play making an occupied bed with a classmate. Take turns being the nursing assistant and the person in the bed. Answer the questions about the experience.

SITUATION: Kevin Myers, 87, has arthritis. He has severe joint pain and is on complete bed rest at present. You plan to change his bed after completing his bath. He can turn fairly well, but you must be careful to keep his legs in good alignment with a firm pillow between them. Consider these questions about how you carried out this procedure as the nursing assistant.

- How did you determine what linens you needed? In what order did you gather the linens?
- What did you tell Mr. Myers about the procedure? How did you provide for his privacy?

- What was your first step? How did you position Mr. Myers? How did you provide for his safety?
- How well were you able to keep the dirty and clean linens separated?
- What difficulties did you have in following the correct procedure?
- What suggestions did your classmate have for you to make it more comfortable for the person in the bed?
- What changes will you make the next time you make an occupied bed?

3 Make a list in a small notebook or on an index card of the correct order of gathering linens. Carry this with you when you are in the clinical area to help you remember to be organized. Soon you will be able to gather the linens without a reminder.

CAREER PREPARATIONS

Fill-in-the-Blanks

Fill in the word or phrase that best completes the sentence or answers the question.

1 Keeping the bed clean, dry, and wrinkle free will help to prevent
________________ and ________________.

2 When is a complete bed change usually done?

a In hospitals ________________

b In long-term care facilities ________________

3 Describe each of the following:

a Closed bed ________________

b Open bed ________________

c Occupied bed ________________

d Surgical bed ________________

4 Why is a plastic drawsheet used on the bed? ________________

5 What is the disadvantage of using a plastic drawsheet? ________________

6 Why should you never shake the bed linens? ________________

7 When making an occupied bed, the person should be covered with a bath blanket to provide ________________ and ________________.

8 When making an occupied bed, what concerns should you have about the person in the bed?

a ____________________

b ____________________

c ____________________

Linen Scramble

9 You are planning to give a bed bath to Mr. Green and then to change his linens. When you get to the linen room, you forget what order to collect the linens. Number the linens you collected in the correct order from 1 to 13.

______ Bedspread	______ Wash cloth	______ Cotton drawsheet
______ Plastic drawsheet	______ Mattress pad	______ Blanket
______ Bath towel	______ Top sheet	______ Hand towel
______ Bottom sheet	______ Pillowcases	
______ Bath blanket	______ Hospital gown	

Choose the Correct Answer

Circle the letter next to the statement that best completes the sentence or answers the question.

10 When you take linens into a room and realize you have extra linens, what should you do?

a Return them to the linen room.
b Use them on another person's bed.
c Place them in the laundry as they are considered contaminated.
d Leave them in the room.

11 When you are changing bed linens, when should you wear gloves?

a At all times
b When linens are soiled with blood, body fluids, or body substances
c When you are handling the clean linens
d Before the person has had a bath

12 Which statement is true when you are making an occupied bed?

a The person gets up and sits in a chair while you make the bed.
b You must keep the person in good alignment while making the bed.
c The top linens are folded so that a person can be transferred from a stretcher to the bed easily.
d The occupied bed is made after a person is discharged from the facility.

13 Why do you raise the level of the bed when you are changing linens?

a To use good body mechanics to prevent injury
b To prevent injury to the person in bed
c To allow space under the bed for cleaning
d To keep the person in good body alignment

Labeling

14 Name each piece of linen on the bed in Figure 12-1.

a ______________________ **d** ______________________

b ______________________ **e** ______________________

c ______________________ **f** ______________________

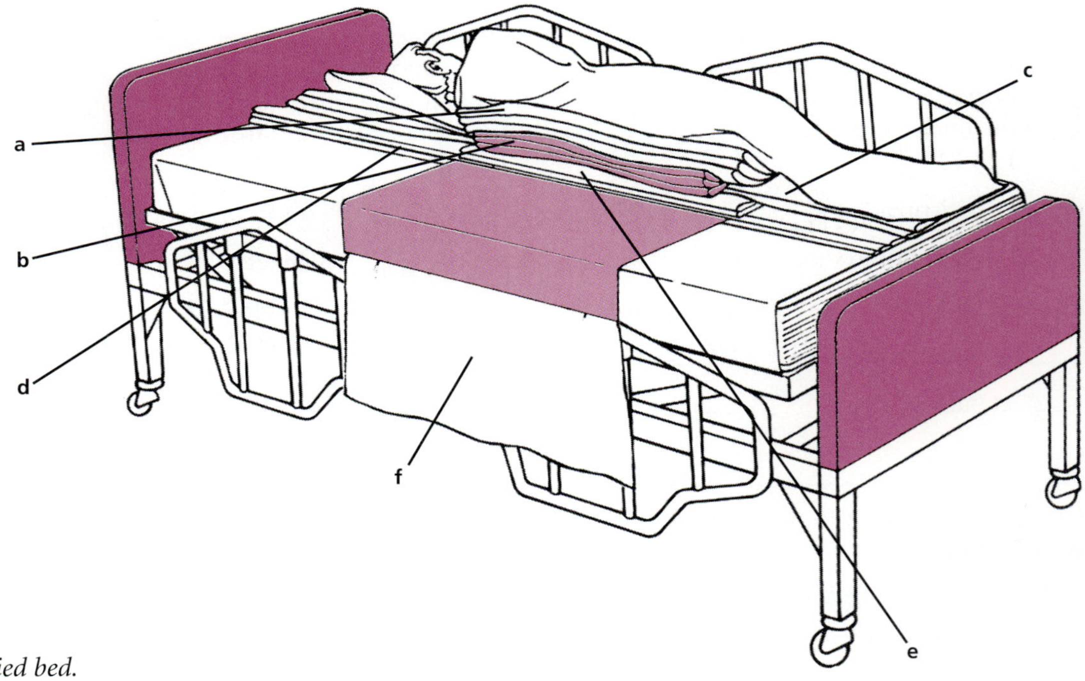

Fig. 12-1 *Making an occupied bed.*

15 In Figure 12-2, A to D, the steps used to make a mitered corner are scrambled. Using the letters under each step, place the steps in the correct order.

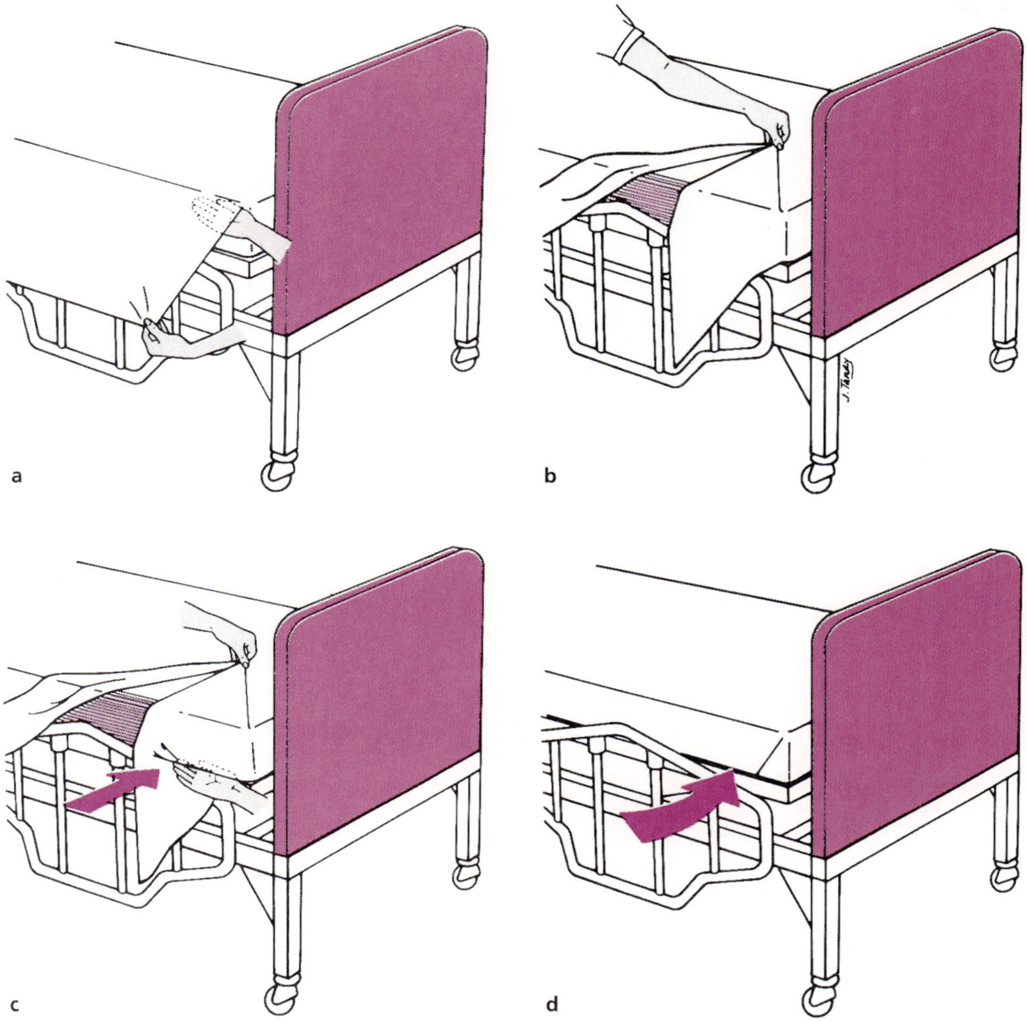

Fig. 12-2 *Making a mitered corner.*

13 Cleanliness and Skin Care

PERSONAL EXPLORATIONS

1 Have three or four classmates answer these questions to discover differences in personal hygiene practices. How does this comparison help you to understand differences in personal hygiene practices of your patients/residents?

- How often do you usually take a complete bath or shower?
- Do you prefer a shower or a tub bath?
- What time of day do you usually bathe?
- What methods do you use to keep skin healthy? Special soaps? Lotions? Bath oils?
- When do you prefer to brush your teeth? How many times a day do you brush? How often do you floss? What type of brush and toothpaste do you prefer?
- What type of deodorant or antiperspirant do you use? Roll-on? Spray?

2 Role play this situation with a classmate. Take turns being the nursing assistant and the person receiving the backrub.

SITUATION: You are assigned to give Mary Leland a backrub at bedtime. You know that she is confused and cannot communicate with you, so you cannot ask her how she likes to have her backrub done. You try a variety of strokes and techniques in an effort to make Mrs. Leland comfortable. Consider these questions about how you felt when you were "Mrs. Leland."

- How did the lotion feel on your back? Was it warm or cold?
- Which strokes were more relaxing? More stimulating? Which did you prefer?
- How long do you think that the backrub lasted?
- How did you know that the backrub was ending? What nonverbal clues did you sense?
- What would you like to tell the person giving the backrub that would improve the technique used?

3 Using the directions in Chapter 13 of your textbook, make a padded tongue blade that could be used when giving oral hygiene. What is the purpose of the padded tongue blade?

4 Role play this situation with a classmate. Take turns as the nursing assistant and the person receiving oral care.

SITUATION: Carrie, 16, fractured both wrists when she fell while rollerblading. You are assigned to provide oral hygiene, including flossing.

Consider these questions about how you felt when you were "Carrie."

- What did the nursing assistant explain to you before the oral hygiene was done?
- What choices were you given? About positioning or equipment? About products used? About techniques used?
- How did it feel to have someone else give you oral care? Flossing your teeth?
- How clean did your teeth feel when the oral care was completed?
- What would you like to tell the person giving the oral care about the techniques used?

CAREER PREPARATIONS

Cleanliness

Crossword

ACROSS

3. Perineal care
6. Practice of maintaining cleanliness of a person
7. Plaque
8. Fluffy pad used to protect person's skin from irritating bed linens
10. Foam mattress with peaks that help to distribute weight more evenly
12. Armpit
13. Pertaining to the mouth

DOWN

1. Bedsore or pressure sore
2. Breathing of fluid or an object into the lungs
4. Occurs when skin sticks to a surface and underlying tissue moves
5. Spongy foam attached to a stick, used to give oral care
9. Tubelike structure that normally allows urine to drain from bladder to outside body
11. White part of the eye

Matching

Match the following statements with the time the care described is usually given. Some of the descriptions will have more than one answer. List all correct answers.

- **a** AM care
- **b** Morning care
- **c** Afternoon care
- **d** HS care

1 ______ Shaving a person

2 ______ Placing a person in Fowler's position or in chair

3 ______ Giving a back massage

4 ______ Helping a person to undress and put on pajamas

5 ______ Offering a bedpan or urinal

6 ______ Brushing or combing a person's hair

7 ______ Providing shower, tub bath, or bed bath

8 ______ Assisting with oral care

Match the stage of a pressure sore with the correct description.

- **a** Stage 1
- **b** Stage 2
- **c** Stage 3
- **d** Stage 4

9 ______ The skin is gone and underlying tissues are exposed.

10 ______ The skin cracks, blisters, and peels.

11 ______ Drainage is likely.

12 ______ The color does not return to the skin when pressure is relieved.

13 ______ Muscle and bone are exposed and may be damaged.

14 ______ The skin is red.

15 ______ There may be a shallow crater.

16 ______ The exposed tissue is damaged.

Fill-in-the-Blanks

Fill in the word or phrase that best completes the sentence or answers the question.

17 What routine personal hygiene practices are performed by most people each day?

a ______________________________

b ______________________________

c ______________________________

18 When should oral hygiene be offered?

a ______________________________

b ______________________________

c ______________________________

19 What causes these problems in the oral cavity?

a Bad taste ______________________

b White coating on tongue ______________________

c Redness and swelling of tongue and mouth ______________________

d Dry mouth ______________________

20 When should a toothette be used as part of oral hygiene?

a ______________________

b ______________________

21 What observations made when giving oral care should you report to the nurse?

a ______________________

b ______________________

c ______________________

22 When you are cleaning dentures, why do you fill the sink or basin with water and line it with a towel?

____

23 What observations should you make and report when you give a person a bath?

a ______________________

b ______________________

c ______________________

d ______________________

e ______________________

f ______________________

g ______________________

Choose the Correct Answer

Circle the letter next to the statement that best completes the sentence or answers the question.

24 When giving oral care, why should you wear gloves?

a You will have contact with the mucous membranes.
b The gums may bleed.
c There may be harmful bacteria (pathogens) in the mouth.
d You may have small cuts on your fingers that could allow bacteria to enter your body.
e All of the above

25 Mouth care should be given to an unconscious person

a once a day.
b once each shift.
c after every meal.
d every 2 hours.

26 What is the *most important* reason that perineal care is given at least once a day?

- **a** To make the person more comfortable
- **b** To prevent the growth of microorganisms that cause infection
- **c** To prevent skin breakdown
- **d** To remove body odors

27 Which of the following is the correct way to wash the perineal area?

- **a** Wash from the anal area toward the urethra.
- **b** Wash in a circular motion from the outside to the inside.
- **c** Wash from the urethra to the anal area.
- **d** Wash back and forth over the entire area several times.

28 Which of the following statements is *false?*

- **a** The nurse may tell the nursing assistant to stop the IV flow rate during a bath or when changing a gown.
- **b** The nursing assistant must call the nurse to turn off the IV flow when the person's gown is going to be changed.
- **c** The nursing assistant may adjust the IV flow rate after changing the person's gown.
- **d** The nursing assistant carefully disconnects the IV tubing in order to change the gown.

Labeling

29 Using an arrow on Figure 13-1, indicate the direction used to clean the eyes while giving a bed bath.

Fig. 13-1 *Cleaning the eyes.*

30 Using arrows on Figure 13-2, indicate the directions in which the teeth should be brushed.

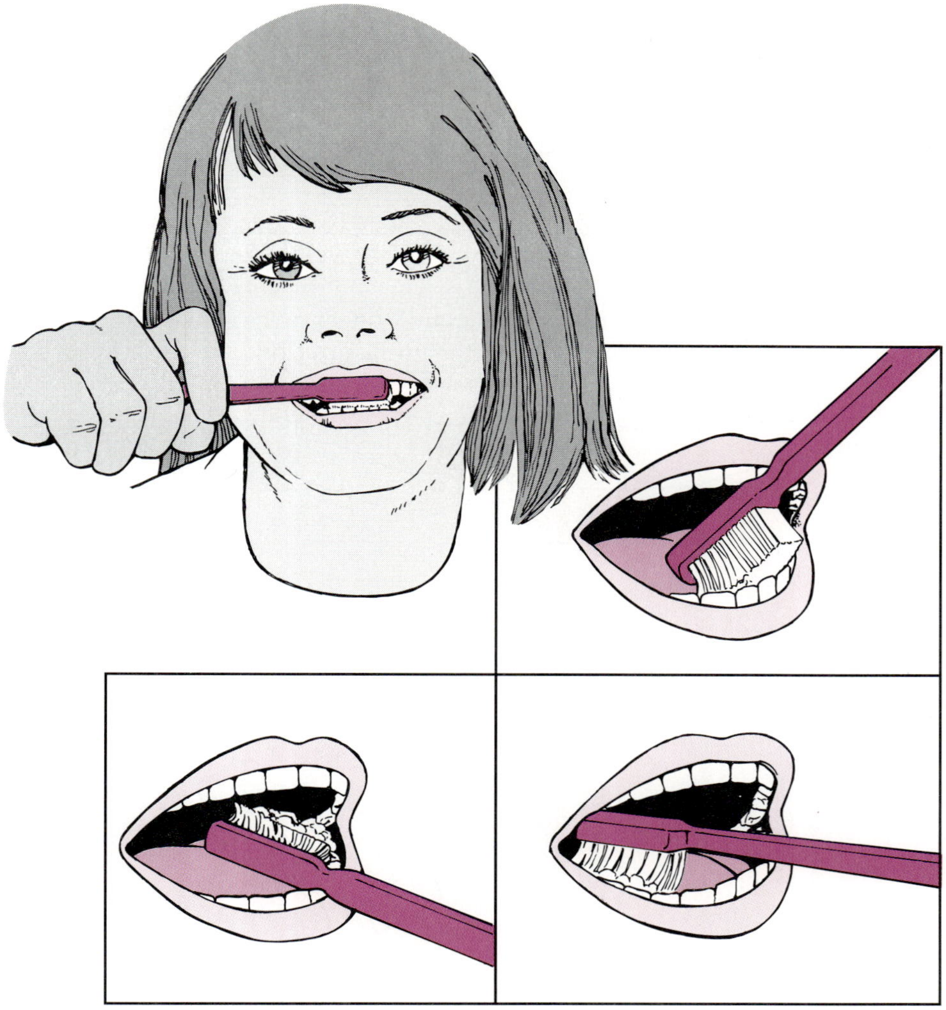

Fig. 13-2 *Brushing the teeth.*

31 Using the drawing in Figure 13-3, place an X on five areas where decubitus ulcers may form on a person lying in the supine position.

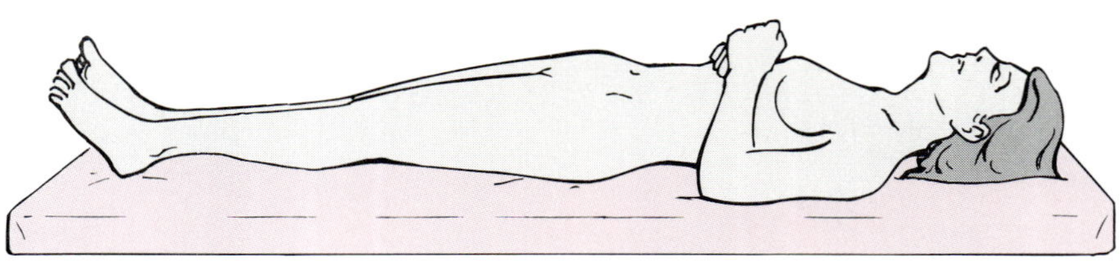

Fig. 13-3

32 Using the drawing in Figure 13-4, place an X on six areas where decubitus ulcers may form on a person lying in the lateral position.

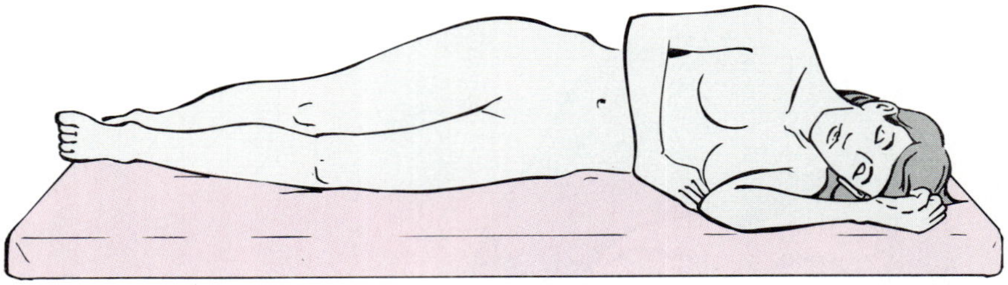

Fig. 13-4

33 Using the drawing in Figure 13-5, place an X on six areas where decubitus ulcers may form on a person lying in the prone position.

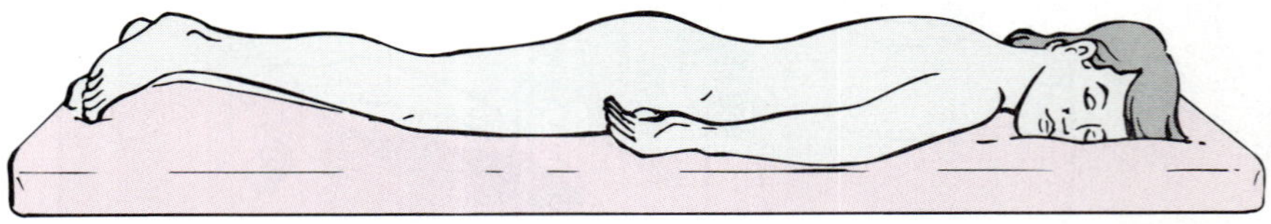

Fig. 13-5

34 Using the drawing in Figure 13-6, place an X on three areas where decubitus ulcers may form on a person lying in the Fowler's position.

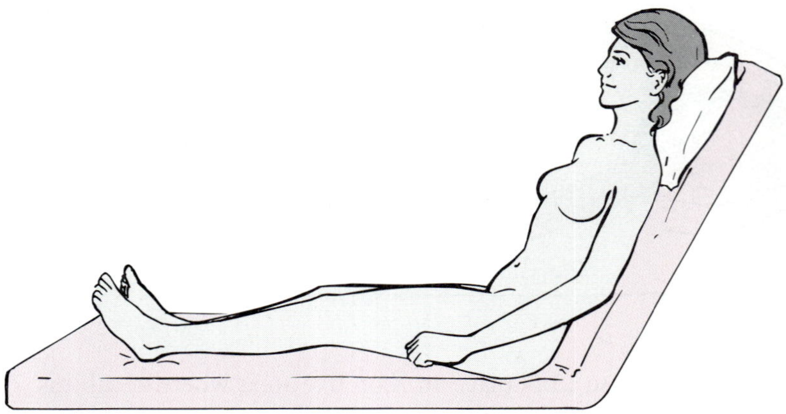

Fig. 13-6

35 Using the drawing in Figure 13-7, place an X on four areas where decubitus ulcers may form on a person in the sitting position.

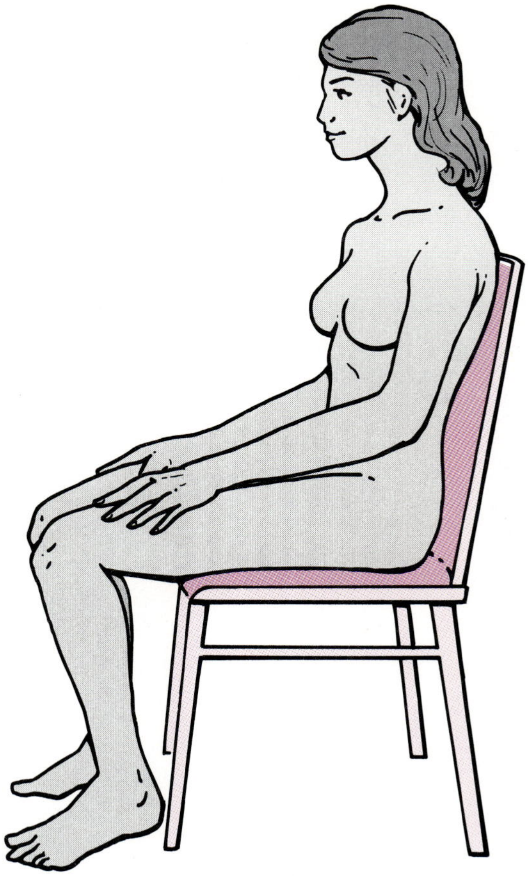

Fig. 13-7

14 Personal Care and Grooming

PERSONAL EXPLORATIONS

1 If you are a female, ask a male friend or family member to allow you to shave him with a nonelectric razor. If you are a male, ask a female friend or family member to allow you to shave her legs with a nonelectric razor. Answer these questions about shaving someone other than yourself. Ask the person you are shaving to help you answer some of the questions.

- What type of equipment works best? New or used blade or razor? Safety razor or disposable razor?
- What difference does it make if you use shaving cream? Soapy lather? Water alone?
- What happens if you try to shave someone without any lubricant such as shaving cream? How does the skin feel? How does the razor move across the skin? What problem(s) may occur if this method is used?
- Which technique makes shaving easier? When you apply more pressure? Less pressure? Shaving against the hair growth? With the hair growth?
- Shave one leg or one side of the face with the hair growth and the other leg or side of the face against the hair growth. Ask your partner to report any difference in the hair growth during the next day or two. What was the result?
- How can the person you are shaving make it easier to get a close shave?
- What did you find difficult to shave? How did you deal with these areas?
- Ask the person you shaved to give you any tips on how to improve when you shave someone else.

2 Role play this situation with a classmate. Take turns being the nursing assistant and the person being dressed. When you are acting as Mr. Olson, remember to keep your left arm and leg limp. Answer the questions about dressing a person.

SITUATION: Timothy Olson, 58, has hemiparesis on the left side of his body. You are assigned to help him dress in regular clothes after breakfast. He is sitting in a chair in his room wearing pajamas, a robe, and slippers. His fresh clothes are on the bed, including an undershirt, dress shirt, slacks, socks, and shoes.

Consider these questions about the experience.

- How did you provide for Mr. Olson's privacy?
- How did you position Mr. Olson to undress and dress him?
- How did you remove his robe? Pajamas? Slippers?
- How did you get an over-the-head undershirt on Mr. Olson?
- Which arm did you redress first? Was this effective or did you have difficulty?
- What difficulties did you have getting the dress shirt on Mr. Olson?
- How did you put on the slacks? What difficulties did you have with this?
- How did you put on the socks and shoes?
- Overall, was this procedure easier or harder than you thought it would be? Were you able to follow the directions in Chapter 14 of the textbook to make this task easier?
- Discuss with each other how you felt when you were Mr. Olson and you were unable to assist in getting dressed.

CAREER PREPARATIONS

Matching

Match the words in the comb in Figure 14-1 with the correct definition.

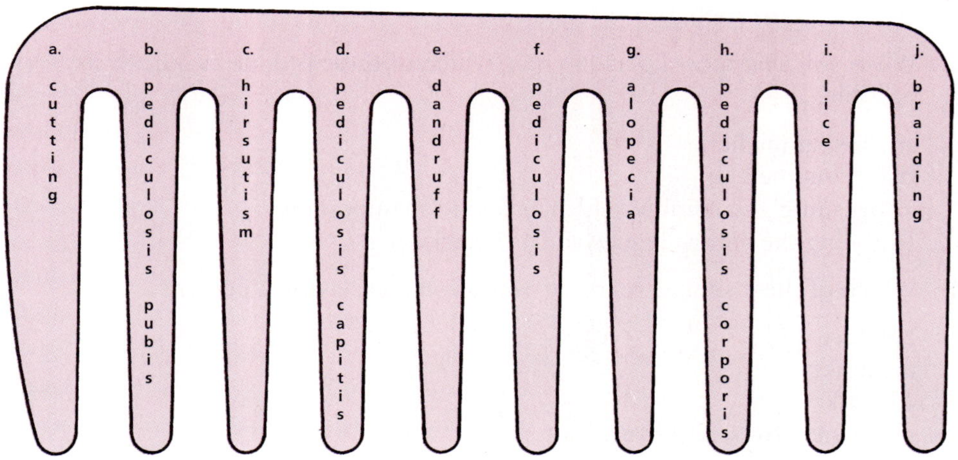

Fig. 14-1

1 ______ Excessive body hair

2 ______ Infestation with lice in the pubic area

3 ______ Hair loss

4 ______ Infestation with lice

5 ______ With the person's permission, a manner of grooming hair

6 ______ Excessive amounts of dry, white flakes from the scalp

7 ______ Parasites that can live on different parts of the body

8 ______ An action that is never used on matted or tangled hair

9 ______ Infestation of the scalp with lice

10 ______ Infestation of the body with lice

Choose the Correct Answer

Circle the letter next to the statement that best completes the sentence or answers the question.

11 A person has long hair. Which procedure *cannot* be done?

a Daily brushing and combing
b Shampooing
c Cutting the hair to remove tangles and matting
d Braiding or styling

12 When you shampoo a person's hair, which of these is done as quickly as possible?

a Rinsing the hair
b Drying the hair
c Brushing and combing the hair before shampooing
d Styling the hair as requested by the person

13 Which of these should you wear when you are shaving a person?

a Gown
b Gloves
c Mask
d Gown, gloves, and mask

14 Which of the following may not be done without permission if the man has a beard or mustache?

a Trimming or shaving
b Washing daily
c Combing
d Brushing

15 Which of these statements is correct about dressing or undressing a person?

a Remove clothing from the weak side first.
b Put clothing on the weak side first.
c Put clothing on the strong side first.
d Remove clothing from the side farthest away from you first.

16 Which of these steps is correct when you change a gown for a person with an IV?

a Remove the gown from the arm with the IV first.
b Gather up the sleeve of the arm with the IV and slide it over the IV site and tubing.
c Turn off the IV and disconnect it temporarily while changing the gown.
d Put the gown on the arm without the IV first.

17 If a person is unable to dress and undress independently, where should you change the person's clothes?

a In a chair
b In the person's bed
c In the bathroom
d On a stretcher

Fill-in-the-Blanks

Fill in the word or phrase that best completes the sentence or answers the question.

18 What should you do if the person asks to have a shampoo?

____

19 Why is a towel placed over the edge of the sink when shampooing?

____

20 When you are giving foot care, what is one action you must not do?

____

21 What two skin problems are reported to the nurse when observed during foot care?

a ______________________________

b ______________________________

22 Number the following steps in the correct order for undressing a person.

______ Remove pullover garments.

______ Remove garments that open in the front.

______ Cover the person with a bath blanket.

______ Undo buttons, zippers, or ties on garments that open in the front.

______ Remove pants or slacks.

______ Remove garments that open in the back.

Word Jumbler

23 Unscramble the terms and use the circled letters to make a word that completes the sentence.

a P O L A C I A E

_ _ _ _ _ _ _ ◯

b S U I T H I S R M

◯ _ _ _ _ _ _ _ _

c N A R F D U D F

_ _ _ _ ◯ _ _ _

d D U L E S O P I C I S

_ _ _ ◯ _ _ _ _ _ _ _

e All of these terms are related to _ _ _ _ care.

Word Search

Complete the statements, then circle or highlight the words in the puzzle.

U	P	A	W	G	N	I	S	S	E	R	D	B
C	S	H	A	V	I	N	G	L	O	V	E	R
H	U	A	Y	T	E	F	A	S	L	O	V	U
A	P	I	D	S	E	C	U	R	I	T	Y	S
N	I	R	O	L	I	V	E	S	A	K	W	H
G	N	I	B	M	O	C	S	T	N	A	P	I
E	V	O	L	G	E	R	A	C	L	E	A	N
P	U	E	K	A	M	A	N	L	N	W	O	G
S	H	A	M	P	O	O	I	N	G	O	O	D

24 Cleanliness and skin care meet basic ________________ and ________________ and ________________ needs.

25 Grooming measures include ________________ care, ________________, ________________ care, and ________________.

26 ________________ and ________________ hair is done as part of morning care and when needed.

27 Patients/residents often need help ________________.

28 Wearing ________________ can improve one's body image and self-esteem.

29 When changing a patient's/resident's ________________, it is removed from the ________________ arm first.

30 The clean one is put on the ________________ arm first.

15 Urinary Elimination

PERSONAL EXPLORATIONS

1 Role play this situation with a classmate. Take turns being the nursing assistant and the person using the bedpan.

SITUATION: Deborah Donnelly, 70, must use the bedpan because she is on complete bed rest. She finds it difficult to move easily and usually cannot raise her hips to get on the bedpan. She tells you she will try to assist you as much as she can. You first attempt to have her lift her hips, and when that method does not work well, you roll her onto the bedpan. Consider these questions about how you carried out this procedure as the nursing assistant.

- What did you do to provide privacy and safety for Mrs. Donnelly?
- How did you position her to see if she could help you by lifting her hips?
- What difficulties did you have getting the pan under her with her help?
- How did you reposition Mrs. Donnelly to roll her onto the pan?
- What difficulties did you have rolling her onto the pan? How well was she positioned on the pan? What adjustments were needed to center her on the bedpan?
- What steps did you take to make sure she was comfortable? How was the head of the bed positioned?
- What steps did you use to remove the pan? What difficulties did you have getting the pan out from under Mrs. Donnelly?

- If the bedpan had had urine in it, how would you have prevented spilling during the procedure?
- What suggestions did your classmate have to help you carry out this procedure better with a person in a health care setting?

2 Ask your instructor to lend you the equipment listed.

- Graduate pitcher
- Indwelling catheter with 5 cc balloon
- Indwelling catheter with 30 cc balloon
- Syringe and water to fill balloons
- Elastic tape used to secure condom catheter
- Reagent strips to test urine
- Apple juice

Use the equipment to carry out these exercises and then answer the questions.

- Fill the graduate with the amount of urine usually needed to stimulate urination.
- Fill the graduate with the amount of urine an adult produces each day.
- How much urine can be held in the bladder?
- Imagine how uncomfortable a person becomes if an opportunity to use the toilet is not offered every 2 hours.
- Fill the balloons of each of the catheters with the required amount of fluid.
- When the balloon is filled, where is it located?
- What happens to the balloon when tension is placed on the catheter during care?
- The balloon can be pulled out accidentally. Imagine how painful that could be for the person. What can you do to prevent this from happening?
- Apply the elastic tape from the condom catheter to an area of your skin that has hair growing, such as your arm or leg.
- How does it feel when you pull the tape off quickly? Slowly? Imagine how it feels to a man with a condom catheter if it is applied to hair in the pubic area.
- Use the apple juice to prepare "urine" samples to be tested for sugar. Using three small cups, prepare the juice as follows:

Cup #1	Pure apple juice
Cup #2	One-half apple juice, one-half water
Cup #3	One-quarter apple juice, three-quarters water

Use the reagent strips to test each sample, following the directions on the container.

- What were the results?
- What information would you report to the nurse?
- How difficult was it for you to time the reading correctly?
- What happened to the reagent strip after the time for reading passed? If you read the strip late, what difference would it make in the results?

CAREER PREPARATIONS

Urinary elimination

Crossword

ACROSS

4. An indwelling or retention catheter
5. Process of emptying the bladder, urination or voiding
8. Sugar (glucose) in the urine
9. Process of emptying the bladder, micturition or voiding
11. Frequent urination at night
13. Tube used to drain or inject fluid through a body opening

DOWN

1. Painful or difficult urination
2. Ketone bodies that appear in urine due to rapid breakdown of fat for energy
3. Production of abnormally high amounts of urine
6. Involuntary loss of control over the flow of urine from the bladder
7. Scant amount of urine
10. Urination or micturition
12. Blood in the urine

Matching

Match the type of urinary incontinence with the correct description.

a Functional incontinence
b Stress incontinence
c Total incontinence
d Urge incontinence

1 ______ Leakage of small amounts of urine

2 ______ Continuous loss of urine from the bladder

3 ______ Involuntary passage of urine after feeling strong need to void

4 ______ Involuntary, unpredicted passage of urine from the bladder

Fill-in-the-Blanks

Fill in the word or phrase that best completes the sentence or answers the question.

5 How much urine does an adult normally produce daily? ______

6 When do most people usually void during the day?

a ______

b ______

c ______

7 What effects do each of these have on urine?

a Coffee, tea, alcohol ______

b Diet high in salt ______

c Beets, blackberries ______

d Carrots, sweet potatoes ______

e Asparagus ______

8 When is a fracture (bed)pan used? ______

______

9 Why does a urinal have a hooked handle? ______

10 Why should you wear gloves when emptying a bedpan or urinal?

______

11 Why must you ***never*** use adhesive tape to secure a condom catheter?

______

12 The goal of bladder training is ______.

13 What do you do before collecting a clean-voided specimen?

______

14 In order to prevent the growth of microorganisms, how is a 24-hour urine specimen handled? ______

15 Why is the first voiding of a double-voided specimen discarded?

______

16 What part of the perineal area should not be covered with the urine collection bag when it is applied to a child?

____

The next five exercises (questions 17 to 21) each describe a common urinary problem. Identify the problem and list two causes of each problem.

17 Painful or difficult urination ______________

a ______________

b ______________

18 Blood in the urine ______________

a ______________

b ______________

19 Frequent urination at night ______________

a ______________

b ______________

20 Scant amount of urine, usually less than 500 ml in 24 hours ______________

a ______________

b ______________

21 Production of abnormally large amounts of urine ______________

a ______________

b ______________

Choose the Correct Answer

Circle the letter next to the statement that best completes the sentence or answers the question.

22 Why does a bedside commode make it easier for a person to void?

a It allows a more normal position for elimination.
b It provides more privacy.
c It is more comfortable.
d It allows the bladder to empty completely.

23 Which of the following correctly describes catheter care?

a Wash the perineal area and avoid touching the catheter.
b Clean the meatus and the catheter with an alcohol swab.
c Clean the catheter from the meatus down the catheter about 4 inches with soap and water.
d Clean the catheter with soap and water, starting about 4 inches below the meatus and washing toward the perineal area.

24 When applying a condom catheter, you should use

a a sterile technique.
b universal precautions.

25 When a person is having a 24-hour urine specimen collected, what should you do with the first voiding?

a Discard it.
b Send it to the lab.
c Place it in the large container used for saving the urine.
d Test it for sugar and ketones.

26 Which of these actions *would not* be helpful in getting a person to void?

a Pull the curtains and close doors while the person is urinating.
b Stand next to the bed and talk quietly to the person who is urinating.
c Run water in the sink while the person is sitting on the toilet.
d Stand outside the curtain or bathroom door while the person is urinating.

Labeling

27 Using an arrow on Figure 15-1, show the direction used to clean the catheter.

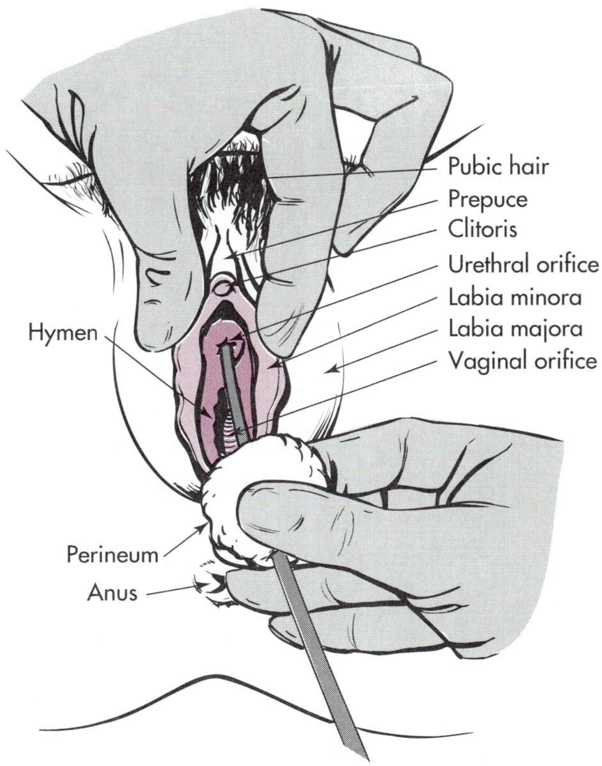

Fig. 15-1 *Cleaning a catheter.*

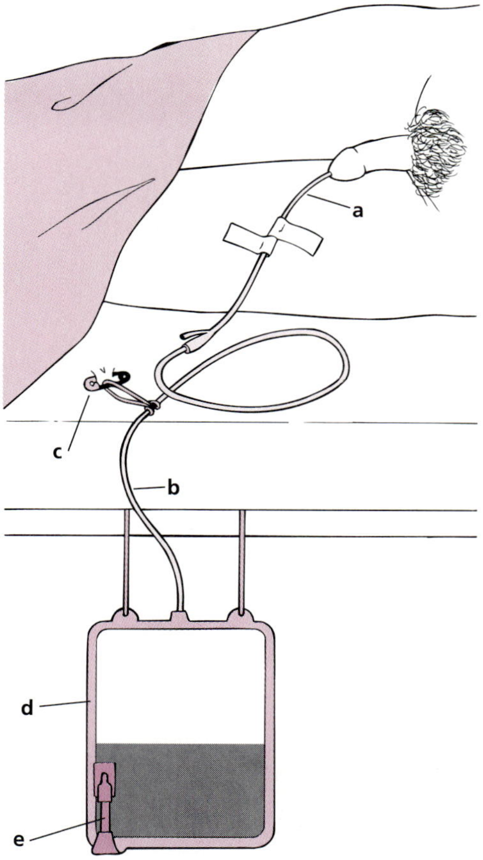

Fig. 15-2 *The urinary drainage system.*

28 Name the parts of the urinary drainage system indicated in Figure 15-2.

a ______________________________

b ______________________________

c ______________________________

d ______________________________

e ______________________________

29 Why is the tubing coiled on the bed in Figure 15-2? ______________________________

30 Why is the catheter taped to the man's thigh in Figure 15-2?

____

16 Bowel Elimination

PERSONAL EXPLORATIONS

1 Do you ever have difficulty regulating your own bowel elimination? Answer these questions about how you treat irregularity.

- What causes you to have irregularity? Foods? Illness? Stress? Inactivity?
- What methods have you used to treat irregularity? Diet? Medication?
- How do you feel when irregularity occurs? What type of physical discomfort occurs? Emotional distress?
- How does irregularity affect your appetite? Sleep and rest? Energy level? Mood?
- What effect does irregularity have on your life? How does it affect your participation in work and leisure activities?
- How can you relate your personal experience to the feelings and concerns of a person you are caring for who has irregularity?

2 Do you know someone who has a colostomy or ileostomy? If not, contact an ostomy support group in your area to find a person who will talk with you about living with a stoma. Ask these questions to better understand the problems the person has daily.

- How long has the person had the ostomy? Is it permanent or temporary?
- What problems has the person experienced in learning to live with the ostomy? How have friends, families, and others reacted to knowing the person has an ostomy?
- What has been the hardest adjustment? What has been the easiest?
- What type of appliance is being used? What other types were tried? What are the advantages of the type being used?

- How much time is required each day to care for the ostomy? What is the person's schedule to care for the ostomy?
- How expensive is the equipment used?
- What leisure activities does the person have? Did the person have to change or give up any activities due to the colostomy? If so, what were the changes? What changes occurred in the person's body image?
- What are the benefits of belonging to an ostomy support group?

CAREER PREPARATIONS

Word Search

Write the correct word next to each definition. Then circle or highlight the word in the puzzle.

I	B	O	W	E	L	E	L	I	M	I	N	A	T	I	O	N	S
N	S	U	N	N	Y	M	A	F	I	N	D	R	O	N	T	O	T
C	U	Q	O	L	I	T	E	E	N	L	E	A	P	F	R	O	U
O	P	U	S	T	L	C	T	N	D	A	F	S	L	L	O	L	D
N	P	A	T	G	E	N	T	L	E	M	A	K	A	A	L	A	Y
T	O	L	O	S	O	L	I	F	E	M	C	I	S	T	O	M	A
I	S	I	O	G	S	L	A	N	U	S	A	N	A	U	T	W	A
N	I	T	L	E	T	P	E	R	I	S	T	A	L	S	I	S	R
E	T	Y	O	F	O	D	R	Y	P	R	I	V	C	C	Y	M	D
N	O	S	T	O	M	Y	T	I	N	L	O	V	E	H	A	H	N
C	R	O	T	O	Y	A	K	I	N	O	N	E	S	S	Y	O	O
E	Y	L	I	F	E	D	I	A	R	R	H	E	A	S	L	M	W
B	O	W	E	L	T	R	A	I	N	I	N	G	P	L	A	N	E

1 ____________________ Semisolid mass of waste products in the colon

2 ____________________ Introduction of fluid into the rectum and lower colon

3 ____________________ Artificial opening between the ileum and abdomen

4 ____________________ Bowel movement

5 ____________________ Alternating contraction and relaxation of intestinal muscles

6 ____________________ Surgical creation of an artificial opening

7 ____________________ Cone-shaped medication that is inserted into a body opening

8 ____________________ Gas or air in the stomach or intestines

9 ____________________ Feces that have been excreted

10 ____________________ Frequent passage of liquid stools

11 ____________________ Partially digested food and fluids that pass from the stomach to the small intestine

12 ____________________ The opening of a colostomy or ileostomy

Fill-in-the-Blanks

Fill in the word or phrase that best completes the sentence or answers the question.

13 What factors could cause stool to change to these colors?

a Black ____

b Red ____

c Green ____

14 What should you observe and report when a person has a bowel movement?

a ____

b ____

c ____

d ____

e ____

f ____

g ____

h ____

15 What happens to the feces when not enough fluid is ingested?

____

16 What role does normal flora in the large intestine have in bowel elimination?

____

17 What is a sign of fecal impaction? ____________________

18 When checking for or removing a fecal impaction, the vagus nerve may be stimulated. What effect could this have on the person?

____

19 How many times do you repeat the removal of pieces of stool when a fecal impaction is present? ____________________

20 Why must you give good skin care when a person has diarrhea?

a ____

b ____

21 What can a nursing assistant do that may help to prevent anal incontinence?

____

22 What symptoms may occur if flatulence is not relieved?

a ____

b ____

c ____

23 What are the two goals of bowel training?

a ______

b ______

24 What are four reasons that enemas are given?

a ______

b ______

c ______

d ______

25 How would you mix the solution for a saline enema? ______

26 What is the purpose of an oil-retention enema? ______

27 How does a commercial enema with only 120 ml of solutions stimulate defecation? ______

28 When you are giving "enemas till clear," how will you know that you have given enough? ______

29 How warm is the solution in a cleansing enema? ______

30 What instructions should you give to a person who is going to expel an enema in the toilet? ______

31 What will happen if you release pressure on the commercial enema container? ______

32 How long is a rectal tube allowed to remain in place? ______

33 What is the purpose of a colostomy appliance? ______

34 Why is the feces from an ileostomy especially irritating to the skin?

______

35 Why are certain stool specimens taken directly to the laboratory?

______

36 What is occult blood? ______

Elimination Scramble

37 Unscramble the terms in Figure 16-1 that are common bowel elimination problems.

a ______________________________

b ______________________________

c ______________________________

d ______________________________

e ______________________________

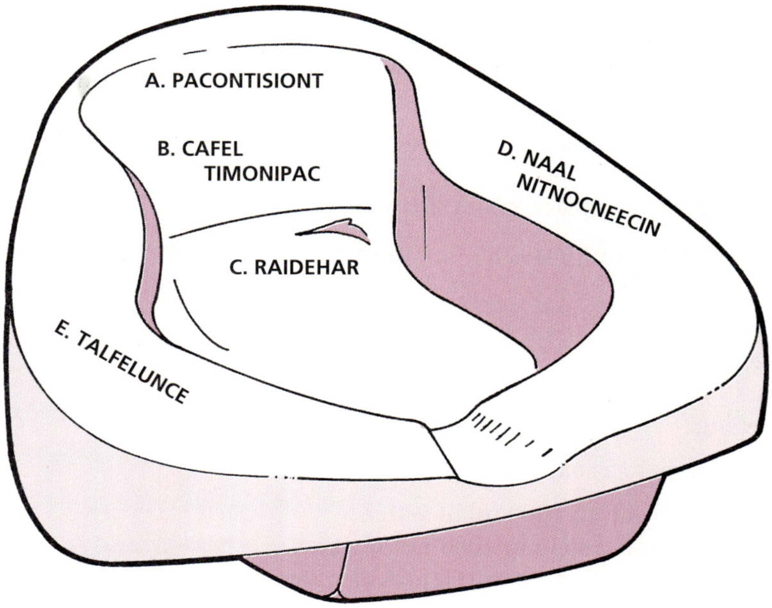

Fig. 16-1

Choose the Correct Answer

Circle the letter next to the statement that best completes the sentence or answers the question.

38 Which of the following *will not* assist bowel elimination?

- **a** Drinking a hot beverage
- **b** Using a bedside commode in a semiprivate room
- **c** Taking a walk
- **d** Reading a book or newspaper

39 Which of these foods would be more likely to stimulate bowel elimination?

- **a** Pudding and jello
- **b** Whole grain cereals and fruit
- **c** Meat and fish
- **d** Pretzels and potato chips

40 Which of these may kill normal flora in the intestine?

- **a** Antibiotics
- **b** Laxatives
- **c** Pain medications
- **d** Enemas

41 When you examine a person for a fecal impaction, how will you know one is present?

a Soft, formed stool is expelled.
b A hard, dry mass is felt in the rectum.
c The examination stimulates diarrhea.
d Nothing is felt in the rectum.

42 What will the nurse be likely to tell you if the person has diarrhea?

a Withhold all fluids.
b Give the person plenty to drink.
c Encourage the person to eat as little as possible.
d Give the person foods with plenty of fiber.

43 What would be an effective nursing action to relieve flatulence?

a Give an enema.
b Make sure the diet is high in vegetables.
c Have the person lie flat in bed.
d Ambulate the person or place in the sidelying position.

44 When the nurse inserts a suppository to stimulate defecation, how soon would you expect results?

a In about 30 minutes
b Immediately
c 2 to 3 hours
d In the morning

45 How would you prepare a soapsuds enema?

a Add 2 teaspoons of salt to 1000 ml of water.
b Add 5 ml of mild liquid soap to 1000 ml of water.
c Add 5 ml of laundry detergent to 1000 ml of water.
d Use 1000 ml of liquid soap.

46 How much solution is usually prepared when giving a cleansing enema to an adult?

a 1000 ml
b 500 ml
c 120 ml
d 250 ml

47 Which position is best when giving an enema?

a Left Sims' position
b Right Sims' position
c Semi-Fowler's position
d Prone position

48 When giving an enema, what should you do if the person complains of abdominal cramping?

a Insert the tube 1 more inch.
b Clamp the tubing until the cramping stops.
c Discontinue the enema and report this to the nurse.
d Withdraw the tube about 1 inch.

49 What is the purpose of a rectal tube?

a Relief of constipation
b Treatment of fecal impaction
c Prevention of diarrhea
d Relief of flatulence and distention

50 What is the consistency of the stool if a colostomy is near the end of the large intestine?

- **a** Liquid
- **b** Soft
- **c** Formed
- **d** Hard and dry

51 Which of these steps would help to prevent skin breakdown around the stoma?

- **a** Clean with alcohol wipes.
- **b** Use an antiseptic lotion or petrolatum jelly on the skin.
- **c** Clean the area with water and mild soap.
- **d** Wipe with tissues until clean.

52 Why should you wear gloves when testing a stool for occult blood?

- **a** To prevent contact with body fluids and substances
- **b** To prevent contaminating the specimen
- **c** To maintain a sterile specimen
- **d** To prevent contact with chemicals used in the test.

Use Figure 16-2 to answer the following questions.

53 How high above the mattress should the bag hang? ______________________

Write this number on the correct line on the drawing.

54 How high above the anus should the bag hang? ______________________

Write this number on the correct line on the drawing.

55 How far should the tube be inserted into the rectum? ______________________

56 Identify the position of the person in Figure 16-2. ______________________

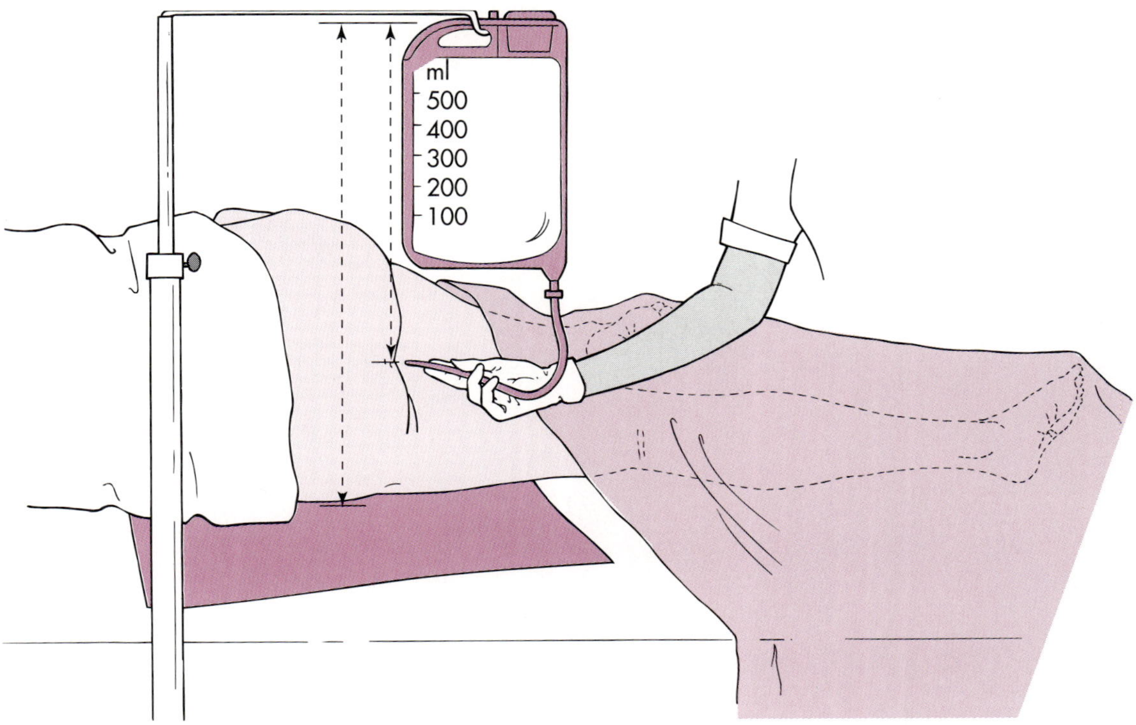

Fig. 16-2 *Giving an enema.*

11

Foods and Fluids

PERSONAL EXPLORATIONS

1 How well balanced is your diet? Make a list of all the foods and fluids you eat and drink for one day. Jot down the list as soon as you eat so that you do not forget anything. Make sure that you estimate the amount of each food you eat. Remember that size is important when counting servings! Organize the list. Draw a Food Guide Pyramid and place the foods into the correct part of the pyramid. Answer these questions about your diet.

- How many servings did you eat of breads, cereals, rice, and pasta? How many of these servings were whole grain products?
- How many fruit servings did you eat? Were these servings fresh or canned?
- How many vegetable servings did you eat? Were the vegetables raw or cooked?
- How many servings of milk, yogurt, and cheese were in your diet? Were these products low in fat?
- How many servings of meat, fish, dry beans, eggs, and nuts did you have? Were the choices you made high in fat or salt?
- How many foods did you eat that only count as fats, oils, or sweets?
- In which groups are you meeting the daily needs?
- In which groups are you eating more than is needed for a healthy diet?
- In which groups do you need to increase your intake to have a healthy diet?
- How did this exercise help you to consider changes in your eating habits so that your diet will be healthier?

2 With a classmate, role play feeding a person. Take turns being the nursing assistant and the person being fed. You may choose any spoon-fed foods you wish. (Pudding, jello, and soup are suggestions.) You should also have a beverage to give the person.

SITUATION: Mildred Stahl, 82, has Parkinson's disease. She is alert and has a good appetite, but her hands tremble and she is unable to feed herself. You have been assigned to feed her lunch. Consider these questions about how you felt when you were "Mildred."

- How were your physical needs (toileting, oral care, hand washing) met before the meal started?
- Where were you fed (bed, chair)? Who made the decision about your location?
- Which food was offered first? Who made the choice? How was the food offered? All of one type until it was gone? A variety throughout the meal? Were you asked what you preferred?
- When was a beverage offered? Was it as hot or cold as you preferred? Were you given a choice about the temperature?
- How was the person feeding you positioned? Did the person's posture make you feel comfortable? Rushed?
- What opportunities were offered to talk or rest during the meal? Did you feel relaxed or rushed?
- After this exercise, what will you do differently when you feed a person?

CAREER PREPARATIONS

Word Jumbler

Unscramble the terms and use the circled letters to make a word that completes the sentence.

1 **a** T R U L U C E

_ ◯ _ ◯ _ _ _

b L I G I R E O N

_ _ _ ◯ _ _ _ ◯

c C I N E S F A N

_ _ ◯ _ _ _ _ _

d P A P E T E T I

_ _ _ _ ◯ _ _ _

e N O S R E P A L

_ _ ◯ _ _ _ _ _

H I O C C E

_ _ ◯ _ _ _

f S L I N L E S

◯ _ _ _ _ _ _

g These are all factors that affect _ _ _ _ _ _ _ _ _ _ .

Fill-in-the-Blanks

Fill in the word or phrase that best completes the sentence or answers the question.

2 Convert the following amounts into cc or ml measurements using this scale.

1 oz = 30 cc (ml)

1 cup = 240 cc (ml)

1 quart = 1000 cc (ml)

a 6 oz cup of coffee = ____________________

b 8 oz of milk = ____________________

c 1 qt of water = ____________________

d 2 cups of tea = ____________________

e 4 oz of gelatin = ____________________

f 5 oz of orange juice = ____________________

g 12 oz of broth = ____________________

h ½ cup of sherbet = ____________________

3 What happens if the diet is high in calories and fat? ____________________

4 How many calories are in 1 gram of carbohydrates? ____________________

5 Why is it important for elderly women to have a good calcium intake?

____

6 Why is protein important to good health? ______________________________

7 Why is protein often lacking in the diets of low-income persons?

____

8 How many calories are found in 1 gram of fat? ______________________________

9 Which vitamins are stored in the body? ______________________________

10 Which vitamins cannot be stored and must be eaten daily? ______________________________

11 What are six common causes of dehydration?

a ______________________________

b ______________________________

c ______________________________

d ______________________________

e ______________________________

f ______________________________

12 How much water does an adult need each day to survive? ______________________________

13 How much fluid is needed each day to maintain normal fluid balance?

____

14 List four religious groups that may not allow members to drink alcohol, tea, or coffee.

a ______________________________

b ______________________________

c ______________________________

d ______________________________

Choose the Correct Answer

Circle the letter next to the statement that best completes the sentence or answers the question.

15 Why are carbohydrates important in the diet?

a To supply products for tissue growth and repair
b To provide energy and bulk for bowel elimination
c To provide energy and flavor
d To supply vitamins that are needed daily

16 What can you give a person who has an order for NPO?

a Unlimited fluids
b No food or fluids
c Small amounts of fluids
d Only clear liquids

17 What effect may cultural and religious beliefs have on nutrition?

a Certain types of food may be restricted.
b Method of preparation may be part of beliefs.
c Certain foods are eaten and others are avoided.
d All of the above

18 What responsibility does the nursing assistant have if a person is being fed through a tube?

a To remove the tube after each feeding
b To give clear liquids by mouth
c To assist the nurse in giving feedings
d To avoid giving mouth care

19 In Figure 17-1, label the plate to indicate how numbers on the face of a clock are used to help a blind person locate food on the plate.

Fig. 17-1 *Feeding a blind person.*

20 How does the method used in Figure 17-1 help a blind person to locate food on the plate? ______________________________

21 The following is the description of a common therapeutic diet. This diet includes foods that are mechanically and chemically nonirritating and low in roughage. The foods are served at moderate temperatures. Strong spices and condiments are avoided.

a What is the diet? ______________________________

b What is its use? ______________________________

c What are four foods allowed? ______________________________

22 The following is the description of a common therapeutic diet. This diet includes foods that are liquid at room temperature or that melt at room temperature.

a What is the diet? ______________________________

b What is its use? ______________________________

c What are four foods allowed? ______________________________

True or False

Read each statement and circle T if it is true, F if it is false. If the statement is false, in the space beneath the statement, change the words to make the statement true.

23 T F The body becomes swollen if too much sugar is retained.

____

24 T F When a healthy person eats more sodium than the body needs, it will be excreted in the urine. ______________________________

____

25 T F A person with diabetes will retain salt in the body.

____

26 T F A "moderate sodium-restricted diet" allows the resident to eat pickles and olives. ______________________________

____

27 T F When a person has diabetes, sugar builds up in the bloodstream.

____

28 T F When a person is placed on a diabetic diet, only three meals each day are allowed. ______________________________

____

29 T F It is acceptable to allow a diabetic to exchange a vegetable with a meat on the diet. ______________________________

____

30 T F A diet that allows water, gelatin, and popsicles would be a clear liquid diet. ______________________________

____

31 T F A person who has constipation may be helped by a high-residue diet.

____

Labeling

32 Label the Food Guide Pyramid in Figure 17-2 with the six food groups and the number of servings for each.

a ______________________________

b ______________________________

c ______________________________

d ______________________________

e ______________________________

f ______________________________

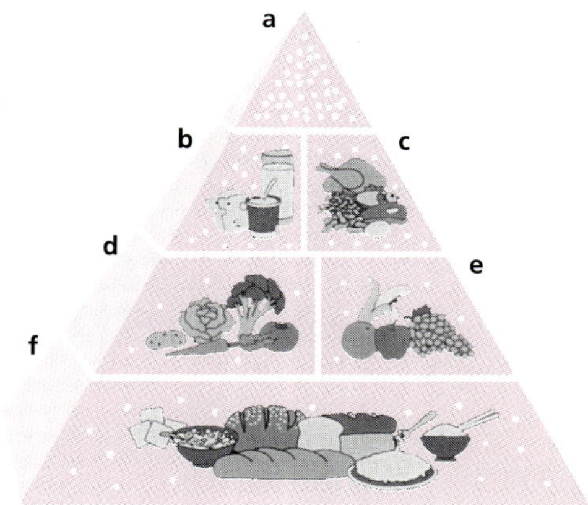

Fig. 17-2 *Food Guide Pyramid.*

33 Using the letters on the pyramid, identify the food group to which the following items belong.

a ______ Crackers

b ______ Kidney beans

c ______ Potatoes

d ______ Pineapple chunks

e ______ Peanut butter

f ______ Ice milk

g ______ Candy bar

h ______ Oatmeal

i ______ Carrots

j ______ Sour cream

34 In Figure 17-3, complete the intake and output sheet using the information provided.

8:30 AM	Breakfast Water glass of orange juice Soup bowl of cream of wheat 2 strips of bacon 1 egg 2 slices of toast Cup of coffee Carton of milk
9:00 AM	Voided 300 cc
10:00 AM	Snack Large cup of eggnog
10:30 AM	Voided 150 cc
12:30 PM	Lunch Cream of tomato soup Tuna fish on whole wheat Carrot sticks Cup of coffee Ice cream
1:00 PM	Voided 200 cc
2:30 PM	Voided 150 cc

DAILY INTAKE AND OUTPUT RECORD
(Bedside record)

INTAKE | OUTPUT

11 - 7

Time	Oral	IV			Time	Urine	Emesis	Drainage		

Total: ______ Total: ______

7 - 3

Time	Oral	IV			Time	Urine	Emesis	Drainage		

Total: ______ Total: ______

3 - 11

Time	Oral	IV			Time	Urine	Emesis	Drainage		

Total: ______ Total: ______

Water Glass = 150 ml
Coffee pot = 200 ml
Ice Cream = 60 ml
Coffee cup = 120 ml
Soup bowl = 180 ml

Milk carton = 240 ml
Large paper cup = 240 ml (like for eggnogg, shakes, etc.)
Jello per serving = 120 ml

Fig. 17-3 *Recording intake and output.*

18

Measurement of Vital Signs

PERSONAL EXPLORATIONS

1 Take turns measuring vital signs on three or four classmates. If possible, use a glass, electronic, and tympanic thermometer for each person to see if there are any differences in temperatures. Write the results you get for each person. Use the table provided to record your readings. Answer the questions following the table about this exercise.

NAME	TEMP	PULSE	RESP	BP
	GLASS ELEC TYM	RADIAL APICAL	RATE RHYTHM DEPTH	
	GLASS ELEC TYM	RADIAL APICAL	RATE RHYTHM DEPTH	
	GLASS ELEC TYM	RADIAL APICAL	RATE RHYTHM DEPTH	
	GLASS ELEC TYM	RADIAL APICAL	RATE RHYTHM DEPTH	

- What type of thermometer was used? If different types of thermometers were used, how did the readings compare?
- What differences did you find in locating the radial pulse? The apical pulse?
- What differences did you find in the rate and rhythm of the pulses with various persons?
- How were you able to measure the respirations so that the person was unaware you were doing it?
- What changes in respiration occurred if the person was aware you were counting?
- What differences in rhythm and depth of respirations did you observe with various persons?
- How were you able to locate the correct spot to place the stethoscope diaphragm to take the blood pressure? What differences in this location did you find with various persons?
- How did the sounds of the blood pressure differ among your classmates?
- What difficulties did you have with any of these measurements?
- What will you change about measuring vital signs on a person after this practice?

2 Practice taking an apical-radial pulse with classmates. Each of you should take a turn measuring the radial pulse, measuring the apical pulse, and acting as the person whose pulse is being measured. Have a group discussion to answer these questions about the experience.

- How was privacy maintained for the person having the pulse measured?
- Who was responsible for signaling to begin and end the count?
- What difficulties did you have maintaining a count for a full minute?
- How did the apical and radial counts compare?
- What will you change about measuring the apical-radial pulse on a person after this experience?

CAREER PREPARATIONS

Vital signs

Crossword

ACROSS

1. Instrument used to measure blood pressure
3. Beat of the heart felt at an artery
5. Rapid and deep respirations
6. Rapid breathing
9. Difficult or labored breathing
10. Slow breathing

DOWN

1. Instrument used to listen to sounds of the heart, lungs, and other body organs
2. Condition where blood pressure is below 100/60
4. Period of heart muscle contraction
7. Persistent blood pressure above 150/90
8. Lack or absence of breathing
9. Period of heart muscle relaxation

Matching

The following words are used when discussing the pulse, respirations, or blood pressure. Place P in front of words related to the pulse, R in front of words related to respirations, and BP in front of words related to blood pressure.

1 ______ Apnea
2 ______ Hypoventilation
3 ______ Bradycardia
4 ______ Tachypnea
5 ______ Hypertension
6 ______ Bradypnea
7 ______ Systole
8 ______ Hypotension
9 ______ Radial
10 ______ Dyspnea
11 ______ Diastole
12 ______ Cheyne-Stokes
13 ______ Apical
14 ______ Hyperventilation
15 ______ Tachycardia

Draw a line from the age group to the correct range of pulse rates per minute.

16	Newborns	70–110
17	Infants to 1 year	80–120
18	Toddlers and preschoolers	60–100
19	School-age children	80–180
20	Teenagers and adults	80–160

Choose the Correct Answer

Circle the letter next to the statement that best completes the sentence or answers the question.

21 Why is it important to keep a record of previous vital signs?

a So the nursing assistant can prove that they were taken.
b The doctor or nurse can compare each measurement.
c The person's family can check to see if the care is being given.
d The nursing assistant can see if readings obtained are accurate as compared to others.

22 When you take the vital signs and they have changed from a previous measurement, what should you do?

a Record the results promptly in the person's record.
b Circle the changes in red.
c Report the changes to the nurse promptly.
d Take them again in 15 minutes.

23 Which of the following steps are correct when taking a temperature with a glass thermometer? (Circle *all* correct answers)

a Shake the thermometer to move the mercury into the bulb.
b Remove the plastic cover before placing the thermometer in the person's mouth.
c Remove the plastic cover before reading the thermometer.
d Remove a rectal thermometer after it has been in place for 10 minutes.
e Take an oral temperature for about 2 to 3 minutes.

24 Which of these statements about electronic thermometers is *not true?*

- **a** The temperature display is easily read.
- **b** If the probe is broken, the person could swallow mercury.
- **c** The temperature is rapidly measured.
- **d** Disposable covers reduce the possibility of spreading infection.

25 If the person is smoking and you need to take an oral temperature, what should you do?

- **a** Provide oral hygiene first.
- **b** Wait 15 minutes to take the temperature.
- **c** Take a rectal temperature instead.
- **d** Wait 45 minutes to take the temperature.

26 How can you identify the rectal probe on an electronic thermometer?

- **a** It has a stubby tip.
- **b** It is usually red.
- **c** It is usually blue.
- **d** It has an "R" on the eject button.

27 How long should you take an irregular pulse?

- **a** 30 seconds
- **b** 2 minutes
- **c** 5 minutes
- **d** 1 full minute

28 When assessing the pulse of an adult, which of the following pulse rates should be reported to the nurse immediately? (Circle *all* correct answers.)

- **a** 98
- **b** 20
- **c** 72
- **d** 50
- **e** 60
- **f** 120
- **g** 40
- **h** 88

29 You are instructed to take an apical-radial pulse. Which of these steps would be correct? (Circle *all* correct answers.)

- **a** Take the apical pulse first and then the radial pulse.
- **b** Get a co-worker to assist you.
- **c** The pulse should be taken for 1 full minute.
- **d** Each partner takes the radial pulse and then the apical pulse to make sure the count is accurate.
- **e** One partner gives a signal to begin counting and to stop counting.

30 You are assigned to take blood pressures on several persons. Which measurements should you report immediately? (Circle *all* correct answers.)

- **a** 150/80
- **b** 180/90
- **c** 150/110
- **d** 96/70
- **e** 120/60

Fill-in-the-Blanks

Fill in the word or phrase that best completes the sentence or answers the question.

31 What are normal ranges of body temperature when taken at each of these sites? (Use the scale [Fahrenheit or Celsius] you are being taught.)

a Oral ______________________

b Rectal ______________________

c Axillary ______________________

d Tympanic ______________________

32 How can you determine that a glass thermometer is to be used for rectal temperatures? ______________________

33 When you shake down a glass thermometer, where should the mercury be when you are finished? ______________________

34 Where do you insert a tympanic thermometer to measure body temperature?

____

35 What site cannot be used to take the temperature if the person has a history of convulsive disorders? ______________________

36 Why is the tip of a rectal thermometer lubricated before insertion?

____

37 How do you identify the site used when you record a rectal temperature?

____

38 How long is an axillary temperature taken with a glass thermometer?

____

39 Why are the earpieces and diaphragm on a stethoscope cleaned with alcohol wipes before and after use? ______________________

40 When you are measuring the pulse, what two characteristics of the pulse should be noted in addition to the rate? ______________________

41 Why should you avoid using your thumb to take a pulse?

____

42 Why do you keep your fingers or stethoscope in place after you count the pulse and while you count the respirations? ______________________

____

43 What effect does moderate pain have on the blood pressure?

____

44 What may occur to the blood pressure if a person stands up suddenly?

____

45 Identify each of the abnormal respiratory patterns described.

a Respiratory rate greater than 24 respirations per minute ____________

b Respiratory rate less than 10 respirations per minute ____________

c Lack of or absence of breathing ____________

d Difficult, labored, or painful breathing ____________

e Respirations that are slow, shallow, and sometimes irregular ____________

f Respirations that are rapid and deeper than normal ____________

Labeling

46 Name the parts of the stethoscope as indicated in Figure 18-1.

a ____________

b ____________

c ____________

d ____________

e ____________

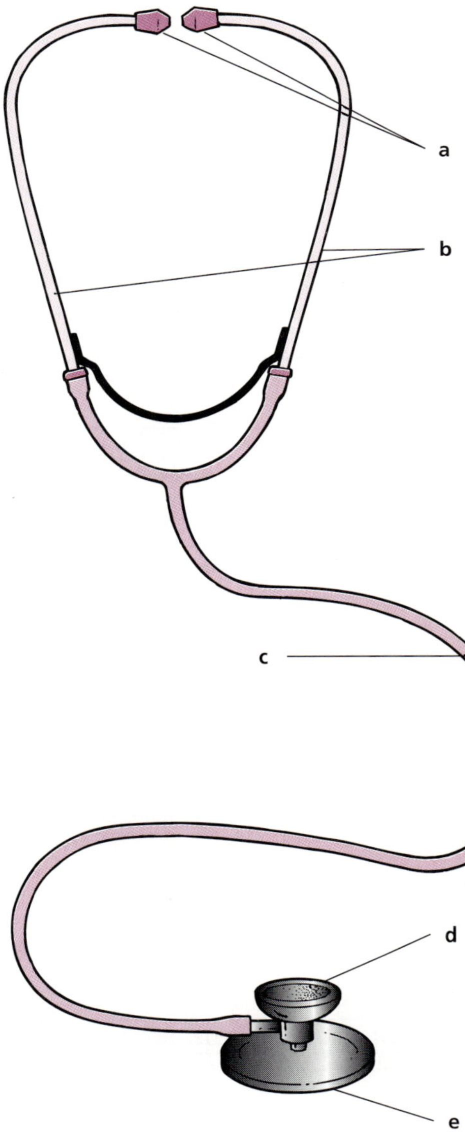

Fig. 18-1 *Parts of a stethoscope.*

47 Fill in the following drawings in Figure 18-2 so that the thermometers read correctly.

a 95.8° F	**f** 35.5° C
b 98.4° F	**g** 36.5° C
c 100.2° F	**h** 37° C
d 101° F	**i** 38.5° C
e 102.6° F	**j** 39.5° C

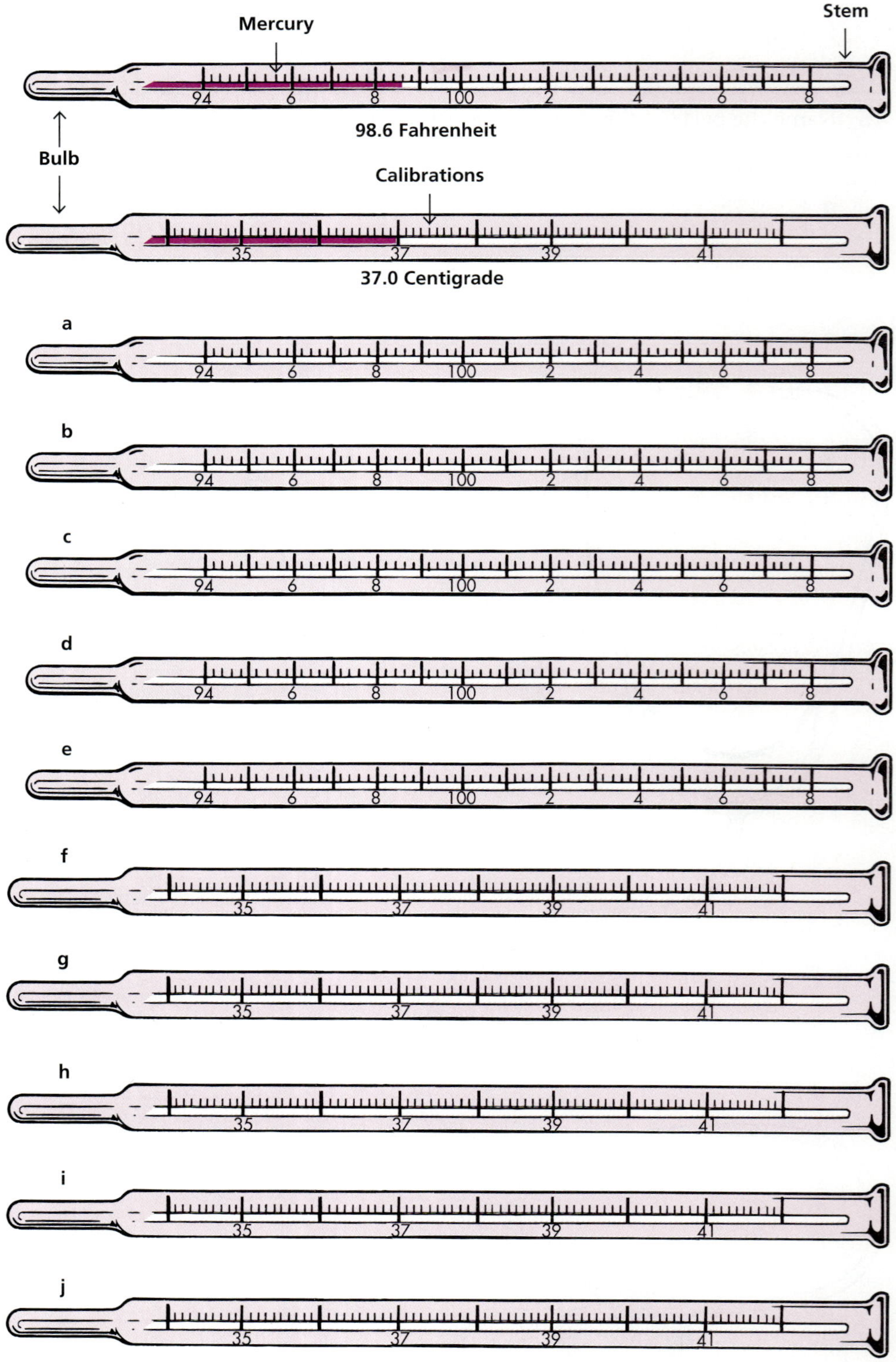

Fig. 18-2

48 Fill in the following drawings in Figure 18-3 so that the dials show the correct blood pressures.

a 168/102
b 104/68

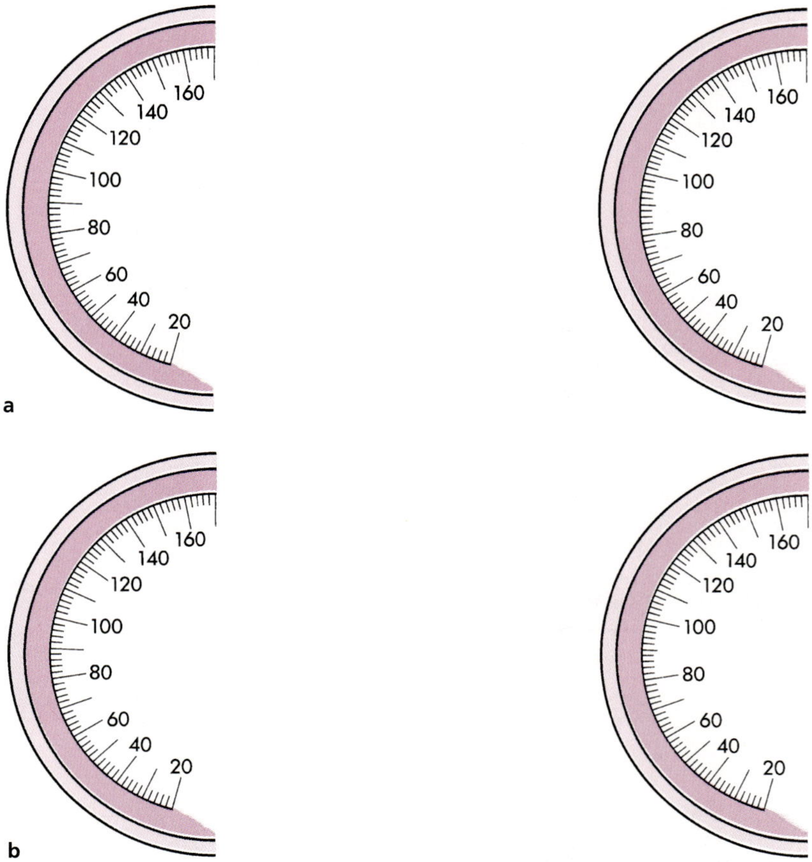

Fig. 18-3 *Reading blood pressure.*

49 Fill in the following drawings in Figure 18-4 so that the mercury columns show the correct blood pressure.

a 152/86
b 198/110

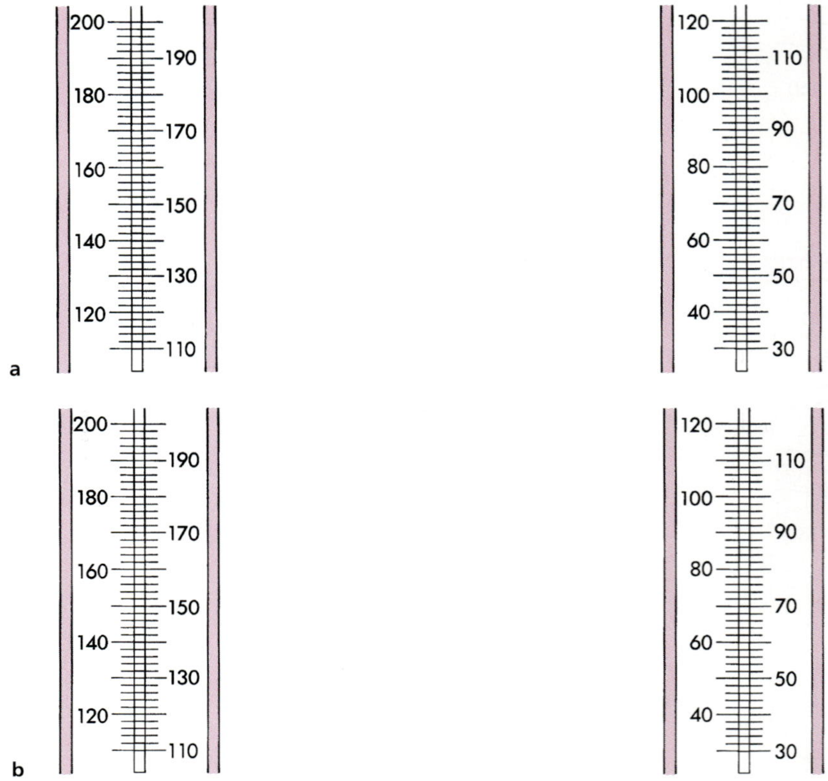

Fig. 18-4 *Reading blood pressure.*

50 The following vital signs are grouped by type: temperature, pulse, respiration, and blood pressure. Determine which vital signs are low, normal, or high for an adult. Then write the signs in the appropriate boxes in Figure 18-5.

P = Pulse R = Respirations BP = Blood Pressure
(R) = Rectal (A) = Axillary

a 96.8° F	**e** 101° F(R)	**i** P = 110
b P = 72	**f** P = 58	**j** BP = 120/80
c BP = 168/96	**g** R = 18	**k** R = 24
d R = 12	**h** 99.6° F(A)	**l** BP = 98/54

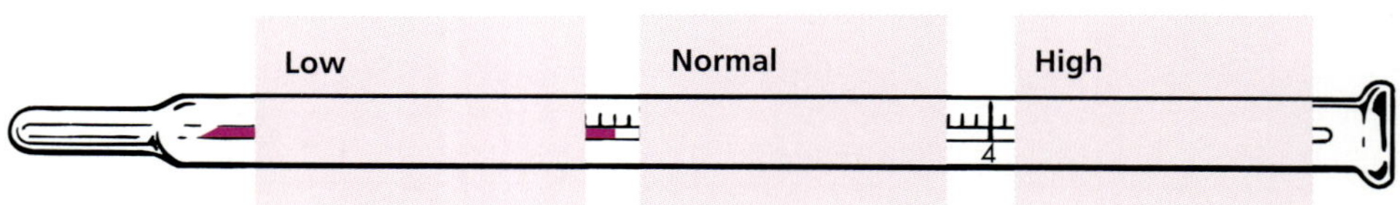

Fig. 18-5

51 Record the temperatures shown in Figure 18-6, A to C.

a ______________________________

b ______________________________

c ______________________________

a

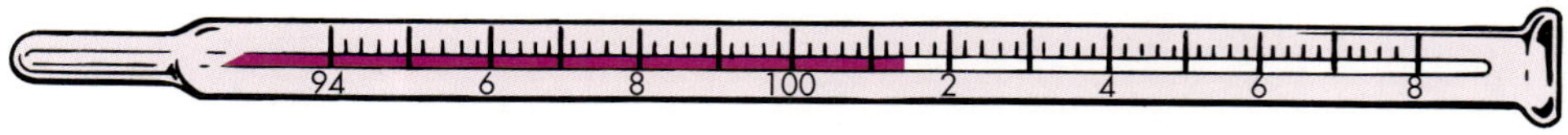

b

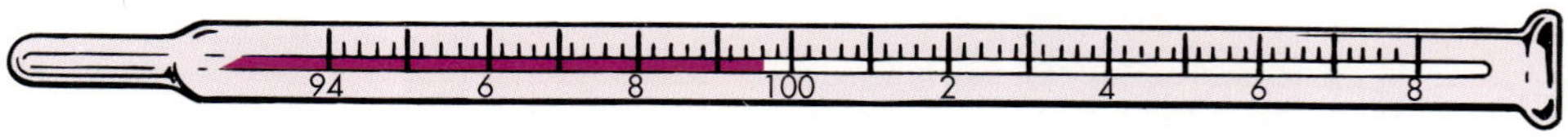

c

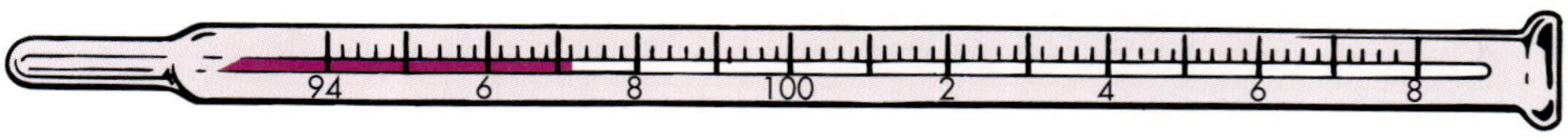

19 Exercise and Activity

PERSONAL EXPLORATIONS

1 With a classmate, role play this situation. Take turns being the nursing assistant and the person with hemiparesis. Follow the procedures in Chapter 19 of the text to carry out the exercises.

SITUATION: Clarence Brown, 52, recently developed a hemiparesis on the right side of his body. He can only move his right leg and arm with a great deal of effort. He can move his left leg and arm without help, but he is very depressed and only moves when encouraged. The nurse assigns you to give Mr. Brown range-of-motion exercises to all joints. Consider these questions to guide your thinking about giving range-of-motion exercises to a person.

- What was Mr. Brown told at the beginning of the exercises? What information did he need to understand what was expected of him during the procedure?
- In what position was Mr. Brown placed for the exercises? Who made the decision about his position? What was Mr. Brown asked about comfort and personal wishes concerning his position?
- How was privacy maintained during the procedure?
- Which joints were exercised with passive range of motion? Assistive range of motion? Active-assistive range of motion? Active range of motion?
- How was Mr. Brown encouraged to participate in the exercises?
- Which exercises were done first? In what order were the exercises carried out? How did Mr. Brown know what exercise was next?
- What will you do differently when giving range-of-motion exercises to a person after carrying out this practice?

2 With a classmate, role play this situation. Take turns being the nursing assistant and the person ambulating.

SITUATION: Lydia Beall, 85, is very weak. She needs assistance to get out of bed, stand up, and walk. You are assigned to assist her to ambulate in the hall using a walker or her cane. As you walk down the hall, Mrs. Beall tells you she feels weak and faint. She loses her balance and begins to fall. Consider these questions to help you understand how a person may feel when needing assistance with walking.

- What was Mrs. Beall told before the ambulation exercise began? What did she know about the distance planned, the assistance that would be given, and what she needed to do?
- How did the choice of clothing provide comfort and safety? What type of shoes and clothing was she wearing? What opportunity did Mrs. Beall have to choose her clothing?
- What other steps were taken to provide for safety? What devices were used to prevent falls? What steps were taken to check the walker or cane for safety?
- What assessments were made when she first sat on the edge of the bed?
- When you were Mrs. Beall, how secure did you feel when you were being ambulated? How did the nursing assistant make you feel you were safe? When you were the nursing assistant, how secure did you feel about keeping Mrs. Beall safe? What methods did you use to hold her securely?
- As the nursing assistant, what did you do when Mrs. Beall lost her balance? What techniques did you use to prevent injury to Mrs. Beall or yourself?
- Based on this practice, what changes will you make in a clinical setting when you ambulate someone who is weak and unsteady?

CAREER PREPARATIONS

Range of motion

Crossword

ACROSS

1. Abnormal shortening of a muscle
4. Bending backward
6. Turning downward
8. Bending of a body part
9. Moving a body part away from the body

DOWN

2. Moving a body part toward the body
3. Straightening of a body part
5. Turning upward
7. Decrease in size or wasting away of tissue
8. Permanent plantar flexion

Matching

Match the following statements with the correct term related to exercise and activity.

- **a** Footboard
- **b** Contracture
- **c** Atrophy
- **d** Bed board
- **e** Plantar flexion
- **f** Trochanter roll
- **g** Bed cradle
- **h** Trapeze
- **i** Range of motion

1 ______ Supports placed to prevent external rotation of hips and legs

2 ______ Swinging bar on the overbed frame that allows a person to move in bed

3 ______ Decrease in size or wasting away of tissue

4 ______ Device used to keep top linens off the feet

5 ______ Device placed to keep soles of feet flush against it with feet in flexed position

6 ______ Abnormal shortening of a muscle

7 ______ Sections of plywood used to prevent mattress from sagging

8 ______ Foot drop

9 ______ Exercise of all joints of the body

Fill-in-the-Blanks

Fill in the word or phrase that best completes the sentence or answers the question.

10 What are the benefits of bed rest?

a ______________________________

b ______________________________

c ______________________________

d ______________________________

e ______________________________

11 What problem can be prevented by using a footboard? ______________________________

____

12 What device can be used to prevent external rotation of the hips and legs?

____

13 What is the purpose of a hip abduction wedge and where is it positioned?

____

14 Using a body part, give an example of each of the following range-of-motion exercises (for example: adduction = move the leg or arm toward the body).

a Abduction ______________________________

b Flexion ______________________________

c Internal rotation ______________________________

d Supination ______________________________

15 What device is placed around a person in order to transfer or ambulate the person safely? ____________________

16 Why do you ease a person who is falling onto the floor instead of trying to stop the fall? ____________________

17 When a person falls, what should you report to the nurse?

a ____________________

b ____________________

c ____________________

d ____________________

e ____________________

18 When using a cane because of weakness on one side of the body, on which side of the body is the cane held? ____________________

Choose the Correct Answer

Circle the letter next to the statement that best completes the sentence or answers the question.

19 Which of the following is *not* a complication of bed rest?

a Urinary incontinence
b Constipation
c Blood clots
d Pneumonia
e Contractures

20 When you move a joint during range-of-motion exercises and the person complains of pain, what should you do?

a Ask the nurse to give pain medication before you continue.
b Stop the movement at the point the pain occurs.
c Stop giving any range-of-motion exercise.
d Push slightly past the point where pain occurs to restore movement.

21 When performing range-of-motion exercises, how often should each exercise be repeated?

a Once or twice
b Five or six times
c Eight or ten times
d Until the person complains of being tired

Labeling

22 Identify the movements shown in Figure 19-1, a and b.

a ______________________________

b ______________________________

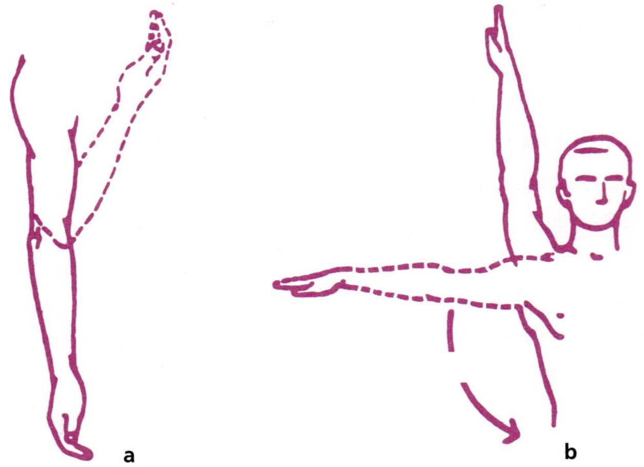

Fig. 19-1

20

Comfort, Rest, and Sleep

PERSONAL EXPLORATIONS

1 Organize a group discussion with three or four classmates to share your personal experiences with pain. Answer the questions to understand differences in pain perception and management.

- What experiences have you had with pain? Accidents? Illness? Childbirth? Surgery?
- How long did your pain last? What type of pain was it? Chronic? Acute?
- How would you rate the pain on a scale of 1 to10?
- How did your family, friends, and others respond to your pain? How did you feel about their responses?
- How did you deal with the pain? What measures did you use to relieve the pain?
- How will this discussion about personal experience with pain affect your approach to a person who has pain?

2 Organize a group discussion with three or four classmates to share your personal preferences about sleep habits. Answer the questions to understand differences in personal preferences for sleep and rest.

- How many hours of sleep do you need every day?
- What time of day or night do you prefer to sleep? To be awake?
- When do you feel more alert? When are you sleepy or tired? Morning? Afternoon? Night?
- How often do you take naps? What time of day do you like to nap? How do you feel when you awaken from the nap?

- What routines or rituals do you practice at bedtime? What happens if you are unable to carry out these rituals?
- What factors interfere with sleep? How do you prevent interruptions that disturb sleep?
- How do you feel when you first awaken? Alert? Pleasant? Grouchy? Tired?
- What routines or rituals do you practice upon awaking? What happens if you are unable to carry out these rituals?
- How will this discussion about sleep habits help you understand variations in sleep patterns with persons you care for?

CAREER PREPARATIONS

Fill-in-the-Blanks

Fill in the word or phrase that best completes the sentence or answers the question.

1 What type of pain is felt suddenly from injury, disease, trauma, or surgery?

____

2 What factors affect pain?

a ______________________________
b ______________________________
c ______________________________
d ______________________________
e ______________________________
f ______________________________
g ______________________________
h ______________________________

3 When the elderly have pain, why do they often require less pain medication than younger persons? ______________________________

4 What effect can pain have on a person's vital signs? ______________________________

5 When a person experiences pain, it cannot be seen, heard, felt, or smelled. How can you know the person has pain? ______________________________

6 How does distraction help to control pain? ______________________________

7 What foods or liquids can prevent sleep? ______________________________

8 How will sleep be affected if a person exercises right before bedtime?

____

9 Why is REM sleep important? ______________________________

10 Several factors affect the amount and quality of sleep. How do the following factors affect sleep? How can a nursing assistant assist the person in meeting his/her need for sleep?

a Illness ____________________

b Nutrition ____________________

c Exercise ____________________

d Environment ____________________

e Drugs and other substances ____________________

f Lifestyle changes ____________________

g Emotional problems ____________________

Matching

Match the symptoms listed with the correct stage of NREM sleep or REM sleep.

a Stage 1 NREM
b Stage 2 NREM
c Stage 3 NREM
d Stage 4 NREM
e REM sleep

11 ______ It usually starts 50 to 90 minutes after sleep has begun.

12 ______ Body rests and is restored.

13 ______ Vital signs gradually fall.

14 ______ Person rarely moves.

15 ______ Person is hard to arouse.

16 ______ Vital signs are much lower than when awake.

17 ______ Person sleeps soundly.

18 ______ Person feels drowsy and relaxed.

19 ______ Sleepwalking and enuresis may occur.

20 ______ It lasts 10 to 20 minutes.

21 ______ Person is easily aroused.

22 ______ It includes vivid, full-color dreaming.

23 ______ It includes the daydreaming feeling after being aroused.

24 ______ Voluntary muscles are relaxed.

25 ______ Mental restoration occurs.

Choose the Correct Answer

Circle the letter next to the statement that best completes the sentence or answers the question.

26 Which of the following statements does not describe chronic pain?

- **a** Pain lasts longer than 6 months.
- **b** Pain is felt at the site and in nearby areas.
- **c** Pain may be constant or occur off and on.
- **d** Pain remains long after healing occurs.

27 What type of pain occurs when a person has an amputated leg and still feels pain in the missing limb?

- **a** Acute
- **b** Chronic
- **c** Radiating
- **d** Phantom

28 Which of these statements is true about the circadian rhythm?

- **a** It is a method of measuring pain.
- **b** Circadian rhythm is another name for NREM sleep.
- **c** It is a pattern of waking and sleeping periods based on a 24-hour cycle.
- **d** Circadian rhythm is another name for REM sleep.

Labeling

29 A scale of 1 to10 is used to help a person tell you how much pain is being felt. Write "least" and "most" in the correct spots.

1 2 3 4 5 6 7 8 9 10

__________ __________

30 When you are caring for children, faces are used to assess pain. Number the faces in Figure 20-1, a to f, from 0 to 5. Zero is no pain and 5 is very bad pain.

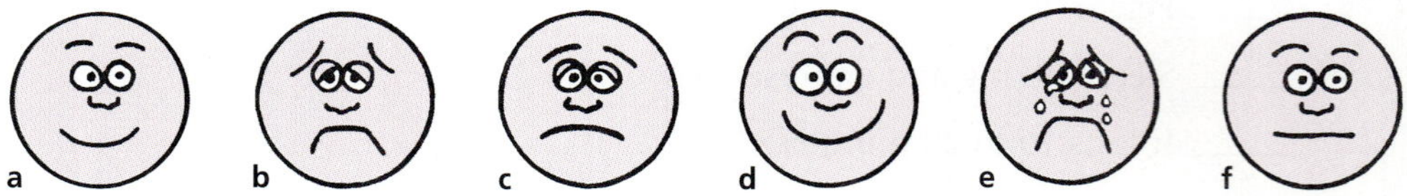

Fig. 20-1

21 Admissions, Transfers, and Discharges

PERSONAL EXPLORATIONS

1 Organize a group discussion with three or four classmates to share experiences you have had with admissions to health care facilities. If you have never been admitted to a hospital or other health care facility, perhaps you can relate the feelings you have had when visiting a doctor's office. Use these questions to talk about your experiences and understand how a person feels when being admitted to a facility.

- Who was the first person you met when you arrived for admission? How did that person make you feel? Welcome? A nuisance? Angry? Ignored?
- Who escorted you to your room? How were you transported? Walked? Wheelchair?
- How long did you wait in your room before a staff member came to admit you?
- How were you addressed? First name? Last name? Did anyone ask what you preferred?
- How many people introduced themselves and identified their title? How did you know who people were if they did not introduce themselves?
- What information were you given to orient you to the room and the facility?
- Overall, how did the admission process make you feel about the entire stay in the facility? Did you feel more positive or negative about the facility because of how you were treated during admission?
- How do you feel your experience and this discussion will affect how you treat a person you admit to a facility?

2 Use this case study to explore your responsibilities when caring for a person who is being transferred within a facility.

CASE STUDY: Rosa Romirez, 55, had surgery for a knee replacement last week. She is recovering well, but is having trouble going up and down stairs independently. Since her house has two floors and she lives alone, she needs further exercise before going home. She is being transferred to the rehabilitation unit and you are assigned to assist her.

Consider these questions about your responsibilities in transferring a person within a health care facility.

- What would you say to Ms. Romirez when you go to her room? What would you do if she seemed unaware that a transfer was planned? Who is responsible for telling her about the move?
- What would you do to help Ms. Romirez prepare for the move? What would you need to do to make sure all of her belongings are moved? What equipment would you need to transport her and her belongings to the new unit?
- When you and Ms. Romirez arrive on the rehabilitation unit, what should you do first? What information would you need to give to the receiving nurse?
- When you return to the surgical unit, what information should you give to the nurse? What other responsibilities would you need to carry out after your return?

3 Use this case study to explore your responsibilities when caring for a person who is being discharged from a facility.

CASE STUDY: Two weeks have passed since Ms. Romirez was transferred to the rehabilitation unit. When you arrive at work, you are sent to the rehabilitation unit for the day. You find that you are assigned to assist Ms. Romirez, and she is being discharged today. Consider these questions about your responsibilities in discharging a person from a health care facility.

- What information should you check before going to Ms. Romirez's room? Where will you find this information?
- How would you make sure that you had gathered all of Ms. Romirez's clothing and other belongings? What should you have Ms. Romirez do in order to document that all of her clothing has been returned to her?
- When you leave the unit with Ms. Romirez, where would you take her for discharge?
- What will you report to the nurse when you return to the unit? What other responsibilities would you need to carry out after the discharge?

CAREER PREPARATIONS

Fill-in-the-Blanks

Fill in the word or phrase that best completes the sentence or answers the question.

1 Except in emergencies, where does the admission process begin?

____

2 What identifying information about the person is obtained by the admitting office?

a ______________________________

b ______________________________

c ______________________________

d ______________________________

e ______________________________

f ______________________________

3 How is the bed positioned when you are expecting a new admission to arrive on a stretcher? ______________________________

4 Why is a person asked to void and remove the robe and slippers before being weighed and measured? ______________________________

5 Who is responsible for explaining to the person the reasons for a transfer to another room, nursing unit, or facility? ______________________________

6 When you transfer a person to a new unit, what should you tell the receiving nurse?

a ______________________________

b ______________________________

7 What should you do if a person expresses an intent to leave the facility without the doctor's permission? ______________________________

8 Convert the following numbers to feet and inches.

a 58 inches = ______ feet ______ inches

b 62 inches = ______ feet ______ inches

c $48\frac{3}{4}$ inches = ______ feet ______ inches

d $53\frac{1}{2}$ inches = ______ feet ______ inches

e 68 inches = ______ feet ______ inches

f 54 inches = ______ feet ______ inches

g 72 inches = ______ feet ______ inches

h 66 inches = ______ feet ______ inches

Choose the Correct Answer

Circle the letter next to the statement that best completes the sentence or answers the question.

9 Which of the following is the correct way to handle a person's valuables such as money and jewelry?

- **a** Place everything in an envelope in front of the person and then seal it.
- **b** Take all valuables to the nursing station and give to the nurse so the nurse can identify them.
- **c** Tell the person to keep the items out of sight in the closet.
- **d** Have the nurse come to the person's room to handle the valuables.

10 Which of these situations with a person you are admitting should be reported to the nurse immediately?

- **a** The person needs to void.
- **b** The person has difficulty hearing you.
- **c** The person complains of pain and appears to be in distress.
- **d** The person cries and expresses a desire to go home.

11 Which of the following tasks are nursing assistant responsibilities when discharging a person? (Circle *all* correct answers.)

- **a** Packing the person's belongings
- **b** Teaching the person about a new diet
- **c** Giving the person an appointment with the doctor
- **d** Helping the person to dress in street clothes
- **e** Transporting the person out of the facility

12 How should you greet a new person being admitted to the facility?

- **a** Greet the person by name. Ask if he/she prefers a certain name.
- **b** Use the first name listed in the person's record to make the person feel at home.
- **c** Use a short nickname that seems to fit the person such as "Gramps" or "Auntie."
- **d** Address the person with the full name, such as "John Smith," to properly identify the person.

13 What should you do if you notice that a person being admitted is restless, agitated, and wandering?

- **a** Tell the person to stay in the room while you find the nurse.
- **b** Put the person in bed with the siderails up and then go tell the nurse.
- **c** Place the person in a chair and secure each arm with a restraint.
- **d** Ask a family member or another nursing assistant to stay with the person while you go to report this behavior to the nurse.

Labeling

Read each of the balance scales shown in Figure 21-1, a to f, and record the correct readings.

14 **a** ______________________________

b ______________________________

c ______________________________

d ______________________________

e ______________________________

f ______________________________

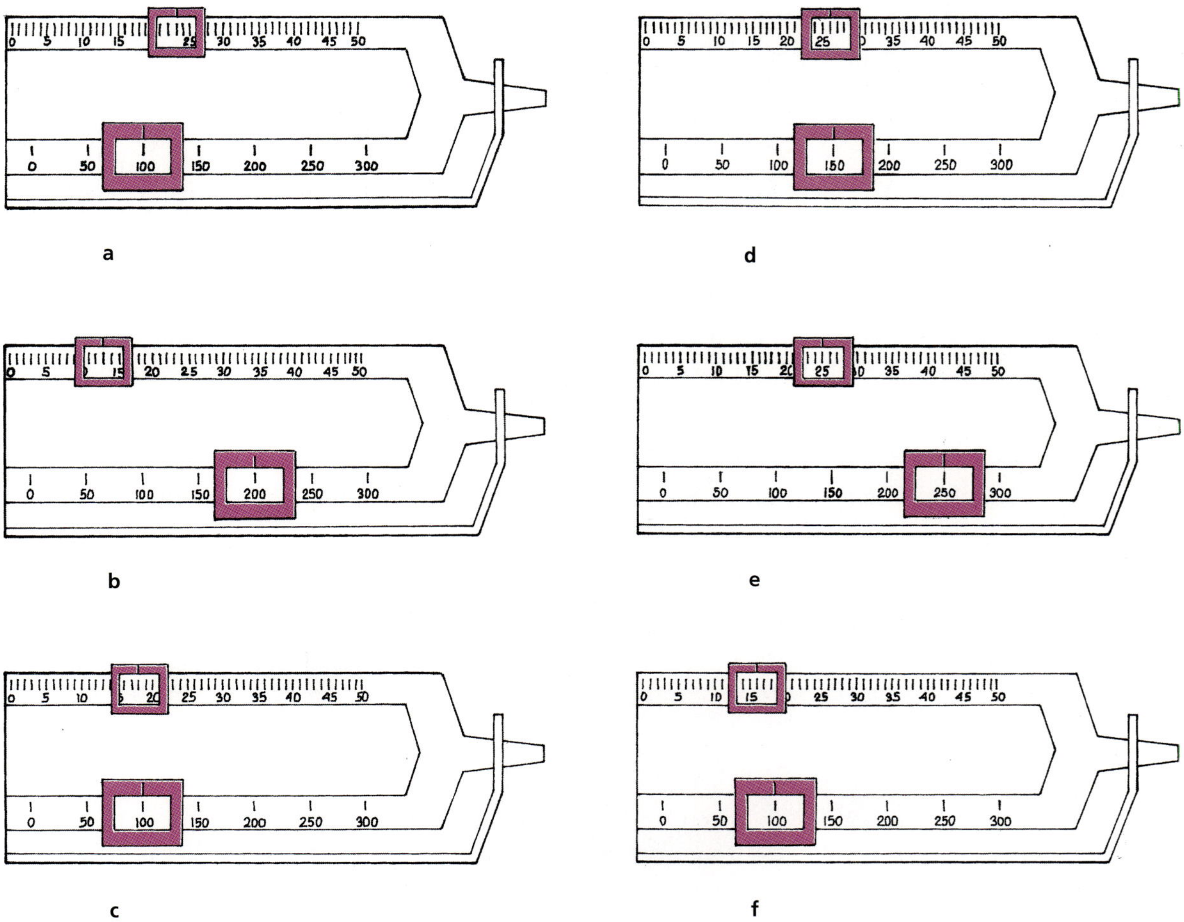

Fig. 21-1 *Reading weights.*

Puzzle

Complete the following statements and find the proper location in the puzzle for each word used.

1 When a person is admitted, a urine ____________________ may be obtained.

2 The nursing assistant may be asked to obtain the person's ____________________ signs.

3 Call for the ____________________ immediately if the person complains of any pain or distress.

4 A ____________________ of all clothing and ____________________ is completed when a person is admitted.

5 If the person cannot sign, his/her legal ____________________ may sign.

6 A weight is obtained with the ____________________ ____________________ (two words) if the person is able to stand.

7 The person will be asked about his/her nutritional and any other special ____________________.

8 Moving a person from one room, nursing unit, or facility to another is called a ____________________.

9 The official departure of a person from a facility or nursing unit is called ____________________.

10 Use the letters printed in the puzzle to spell a word related to this chapter.

_ _ _ _ _ _ _ _ _ _

22 Assisting with the Physical Examination

PERSONAL EXPLORATIONS

1 You probably have had a physical examination at some time. It is likely that you needed one to be a student in this class. Answer these questions concerning your own experience with physical examinations.

- Who explained to you what to expect during the examination? What were you told about any discomfort? Positioning? Lack of privacy?
- What steps were taken to give you privacy? While you changed clothes? During the examination?
- Who was present during the examination? Were you given a choice of having a person with you while the doctor examined you? How did you feel about having (or not having) another person in the room?
- How did you know what was going to be done next? Was each step explained to you?
- What questions were you able to ask? Who was available to answer any questions? Did you feel as if your questions were answered so that you understood?
- How did the doctor or nurse make you feel when you asked a question? As if they cared about giving you an answer you could understand? As if you were bothering them?
- How were you positioned during the examination? Which position in the textbook was used? How did you feel in the position? How long did you need to stay in the position?
- How does this experience help you to understand the feelings of persons you may assist during a physical examination?

2 If you are working with children, it may be difficult to help a child understand what will be done during a physical examination. Use the following case study to answer the questions about helping with physical examination of a child.

CASE STUDY: Samuel, 3, is brought to the pediatrician's office for a physical examination and several injections. His family is moving to Kenya where his father will be working. He begins to cry softly and clings to his mother as soon as you enter the room. He needs to have height and weight taken, blood and urine specimens collected, and receive inoculations for several tropical diseases.

- How would you approach Sam? What would you say to him at first?
- What equipment would you show to Sam? What instruments could you give him to hold? Why would it be helpful to allow him to handle some of the equipment?
- Some simple toys can be made from items in the examination room. How could you use a glove or tongue blades to entertain Sam and acquaint him with some of the equipment? How would these help to gain Sam's cooperation?
- How could Sam's mother help you? What could you do to get her involved with the examination?
- What should you say to Sam before he has blood drawn or gets an injection? Will he cooperate better if he knows ahead of time what to expect? Or would it be better to do the procedure without warning him? Why?
- How could you weigh Sam if he refuses to stand on the scale? How could his mother assist in this?

CAREER PREPARATIONS

Matching

Match the descriptions with the correct position.

a Dorsal recumbent
b Lithotomy
c Knee-chest
d Sims'

1 ______ Hips down to edge of table, knees flexed, feet in stirrups

2 ______ Lying on side with upper leg flexed

3 ______ Lying on back with legs together or knees flexed

4 ______ Kneeling with body supported on knees and chest

Fill-in-the-Blanks

Fill in the word or phrase that best completes the sentence or answers the question.

5 What should you explain to the person about the positions used in the examination?

a ______________________

b ______________________

c ______________________

d ______________________

e ______________________

6 Why is the person asked to urinate before an examination?

a ______________________

b ______________________

7 Why is it important to cover a person with a drape during an examination?

____

8 Why should a female nursing assistant stay in the examination room with a female being examined by a male doctor?

a ______________________

b ______________________

Labeling

9 Label each of the examination instruments in Figure 22-1. What is the use of each instrument?

a ______________________________

____

b ______________________________

____

c ______________________________

____

d ______________________________

____

e ______________________________

____

f ______________________________

____

g ______________________________

____

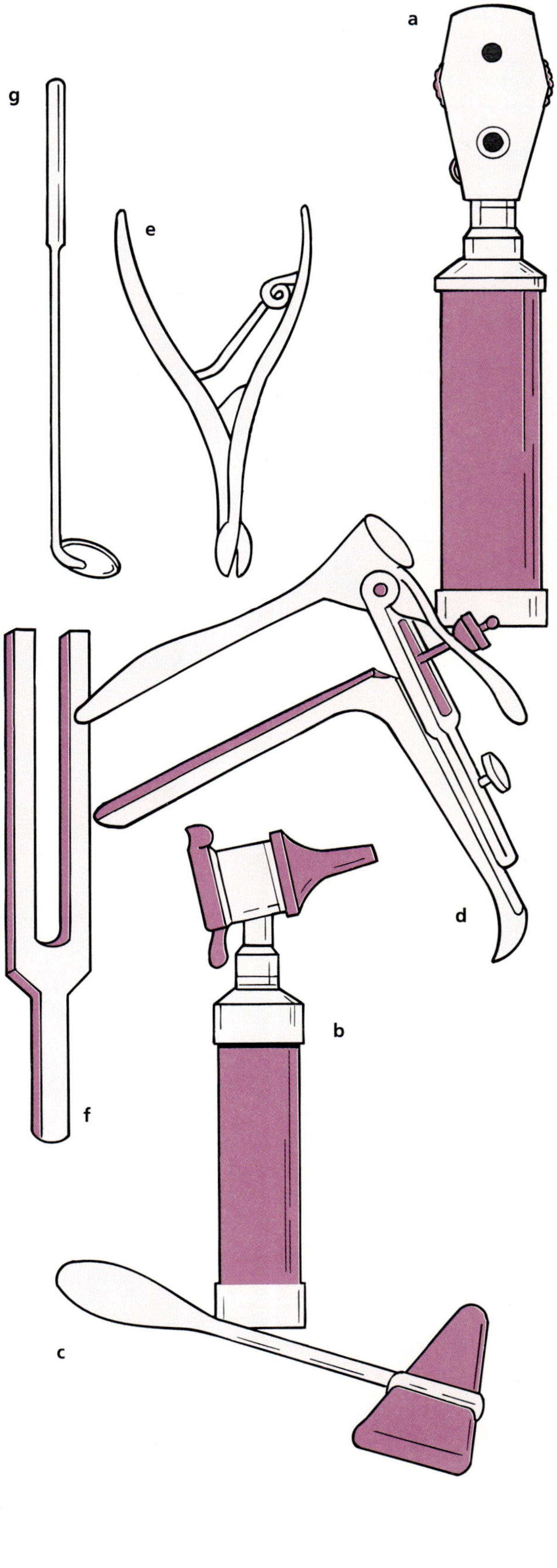

Fig. 22-1 *Physical examination instruments.*

10 Identify each position in Figure 22-2, a to d. When is it used?

a ______________________________

b ______________________________

c ______________________________

d ______________________________

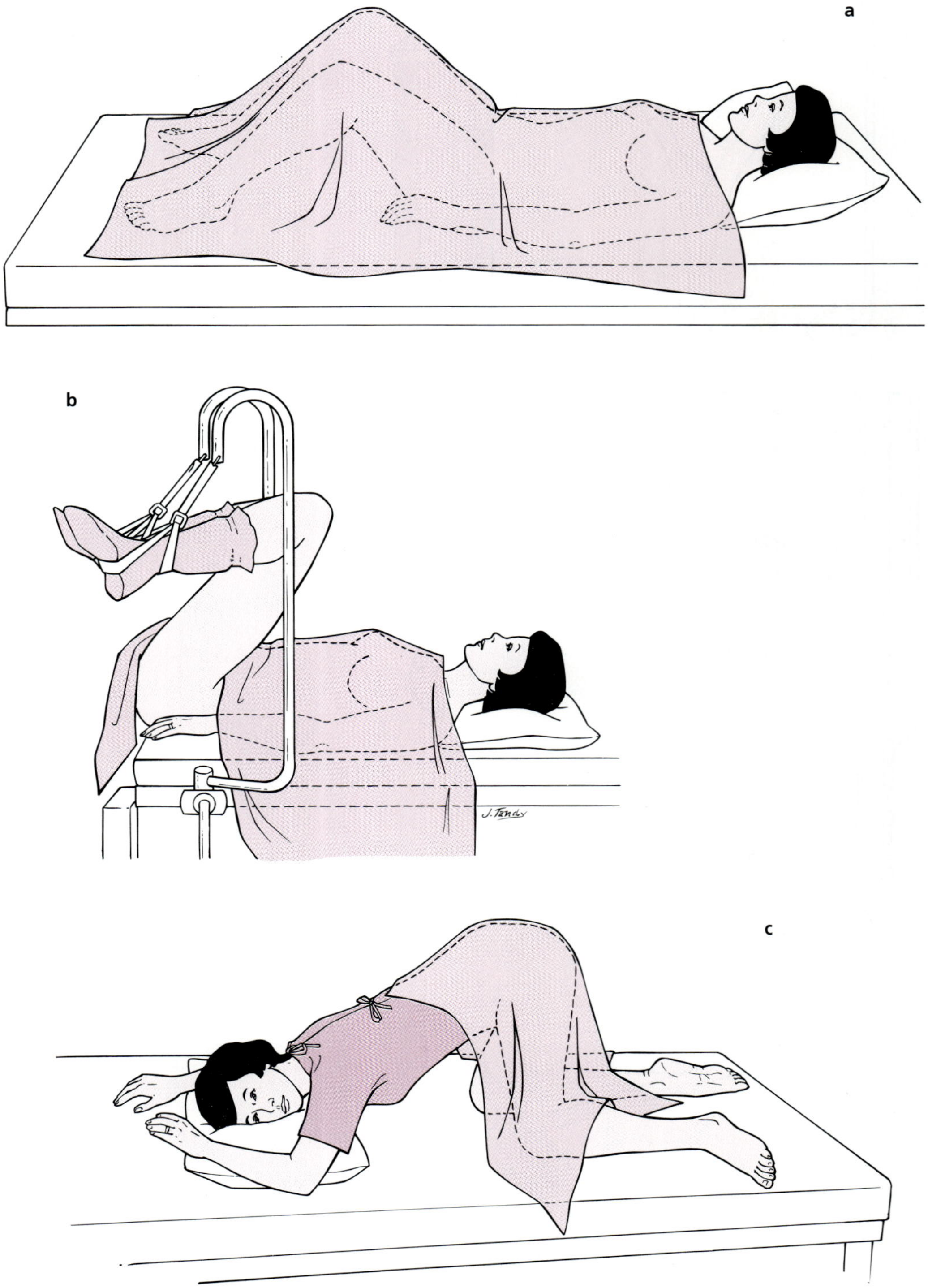

Fig. 22-2

d

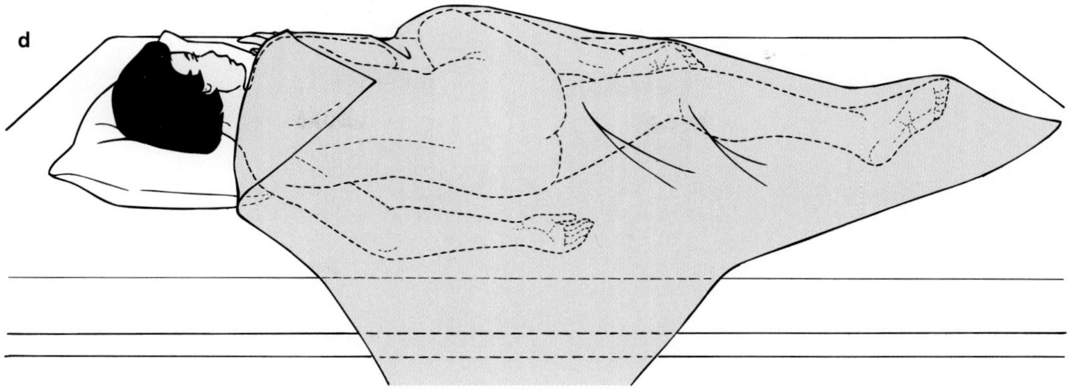

23

Heat and Cold Applications

PERSONAL EXPLORATIONS

1 Role play this situation with a classmate. Take turns being the nursing assistant and the person receiving a heat application to a body part. Answer the questions about the procedure and your feelings about having the heat applied to you.

SITUATION: Robert Smith, 45, has an inflammation in his right calf. The nurse instructs you to apply moist, hot compresses to his leg. Consider these questions to guide your thinking about heat applications.

- What was Mr. Smith told about the procedure before the heat was applied to his leg?
- How did you determine that the compress was the correct temperature?
- What method did you use to keep the compress warm while it was on the leg? What was used to cover the compress?
- How often was the area checked while the compress was in place? When the area was checked, what signs and symptoms were observed?
- What signs or symptoms would cause you to remove the compress and notify the nurse?
- When you were acting as Mr. Smith, how did the compress feel? What were you asked about your comfort?
- How warm did the compress feel at the end of 20 minutes? How warm was the skin in the area?

2 Role play this situation with two classmates. Take turns being the nursing assistant, the person having cold applied, and the mother.

SITUATION: Your neighbor calls and tells you her daughter, Amy, 10, has twisted her ankle. Her mother calls the doctor and is told to apply ice. She knows you are learning to be a nursing assistant and asks you how this should be done. Consider these questions to guide your thinking about cold applications.

- What could be used in the home to make an ice bag? What could be done to make the bag mold to Amy's ankle?
- How would you protect the skin from injury? Why is this important?
- How often should you check the area? What signs and symptoms would you be observing? What response would cause you to remove the bag?
- What would you tell Amy's mother when she asks why the ice must be removed after 30 minutes?
- When you were acting as Amy, how did the ice bag feel? What were you asked about your comfort?

CAREER PREPARATIONS

Fill-in-the-Blanks

Fill in the word or phrase that best completes the sentence or answers the question.

1 What is the difference between open wounds and closed wounds?

____

2 How does a heat application affect blood vessels? ______________________________

____

3 Why is the action of heat application on the blood vessels important for healing?

a ______________________________

b ______________________________

c ______________________________

4 What happens to blood vessels and blood flow when heat is applied for a long time? ______________________________

5 Why are the very young, the elderly, and fair-skinned people at risk for burns? ______________________________

6 Which type of heat application is more penetrating—moist or dry?

____

7 How long may hot compresses or soaks be left in place? ______________________________

____

8 What type of soak is used to clean perineal or anal wounds? ______________

____

9 How long may ice bags and ice collars be left in place? ______________

____

10 How often should you check the skin when cold compresses are in place?

____

Matching

Match the types of heat applications with the correct definitions.

a Dry heat
b Moist heat
c Compresses
d Soaks

11 ______ Applications stay at desired temperature longer.

12 ______ It does not penetrate deeply.

13 ______ Temperature must be lower to prevent injury.

14 ______ Heat is lost through evaporation.

15 ______ Higher temperature needed means burns are still a risk.

16 ______ Moist heat is applied to a small area.

17 ______ Water temperature should be 105°–115° F.

18 ______ A tub may be used for applying moist heat to a large area.

Draw lines between the size of the light bulbs and the distance the bulb may be safely placed from a person.

19	25-watt bulb	18 to 24 inches
20	Large infrared lamp	18 inches
21	40-watt bulb	14 inches
22	60-watt bulb	24 to 30 inches

Match the moisture type with the correct types of heat and cold applications.

a Moist
b Dry

23 ______ Sitz bath

24 ______ Hot water bottle

25 ______ Cold compress

26 ______ Cold sponge bath

Choose the Correct Answer

Circle the letter next to the statement that best completes the sentence or answers the question.

27 Which of these factors may make a person more susceptible to burns?

a Respiratory disorders
b Dehydration
c Circulatory disorders
d Infections

28 Heat should *not* be applied to which of these areas?

a Hip and knee replacements
b Joints
c Soft tissues
d Old fractures

29 What type of wound is a sprain?

a Closed
b Open
c Wet
d Dry

Complications Scramble

30 Unscramble the complications of heat and cold applications shown in Figure 23-1a–h.

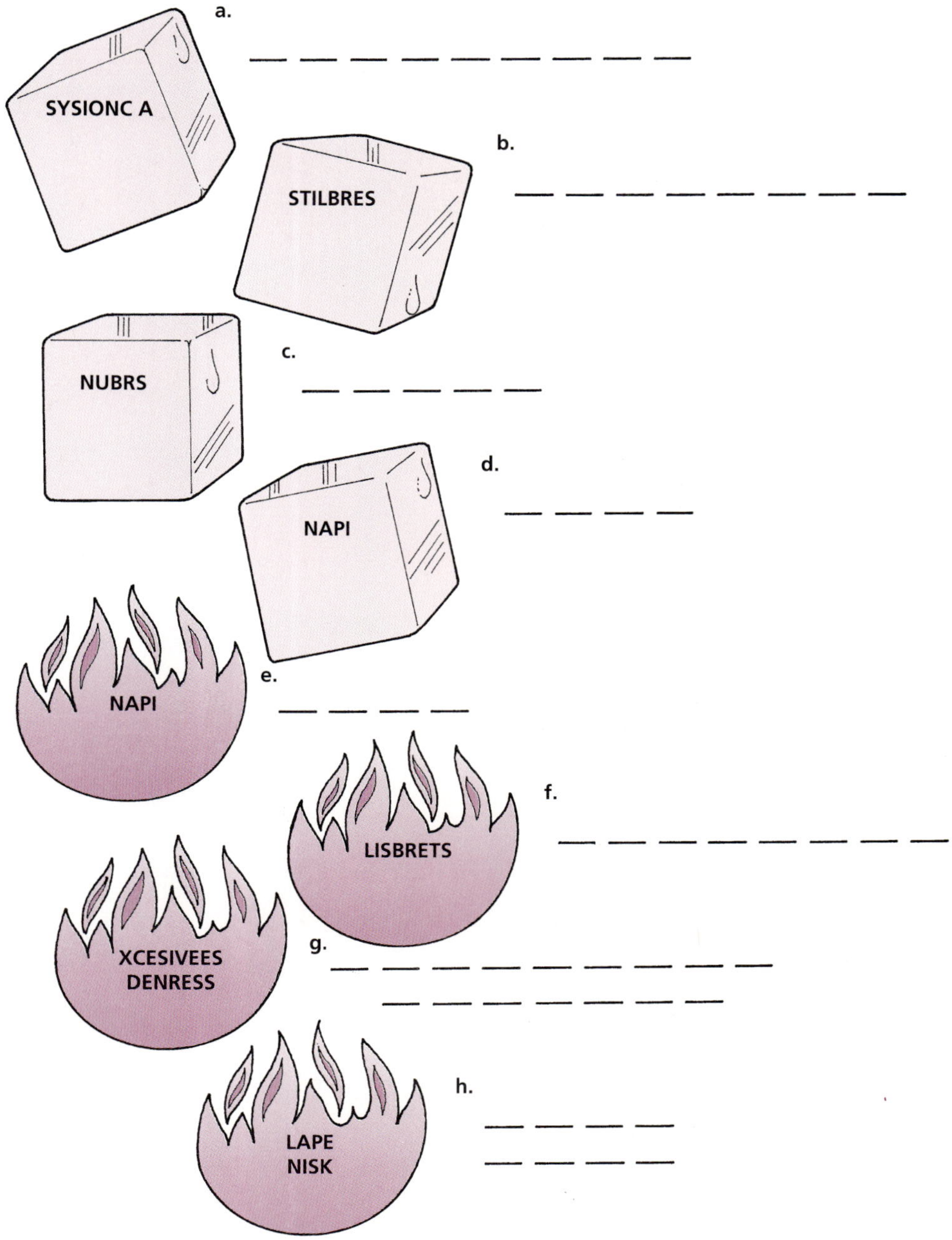
a.
SYSIONC A
b.
STILBRES
c.
NUBRS
d.
NAPI
e.
NAPI
f.
LISBRETS
g.
XCESIVEES
DENRESS
h.
LAPE
NISK

Fig. 23-1

24 Special Procedures and Treatments

PERSONAL EXPLORATIONS

1 Use the case study to answer questions about caring for a person who has an intravenous infusion.

CASE STUDY: Carol Brown, 72, had surgery 2 days ago. She has an IV running in her right hand. It is being infused through an electronic pump. You are assigned to give Mrs. Brown her bath, help her with breakfast, and ambulate her in the hall.

- Why would it be helpful to find out whether Ms. Brown is right- or left-handed?
- What could you do to assist Ms. Brown with her breakfast? What would she have difficulty doing because of the IV?
- If Ms. Brown is wearing her own nightgown, what will you need to do to change her gown?
- How will you ambulate Ms. Brown? What precautions will you take to protect the IV?

2 Use the case study to answer questions about caring for a person who is receiving oxygen and is having difficulty breathing.

CASE STUDY: Sam Roberson, 88, is hospitalized for pneumonia. He is receiving oxygen by nasal cannula. The nurse tells you the gauge should read 3 to 5 L. Mr. Roberson may be suctioned if he has difficulty coughing up secretions.

- What should you observe about the oxygen when you enter the room? What should you do if the gauge reads 2 L? 6 L?
- What personal care is especially important in relation to receiving oxygen? How often should this care be given?
- What areas could have skin irritation or skin breakdown due to the nasal cannula? What can you do to prevent this problem?
- What signs and symptoms would tell you Mr. Roberson was having difficulty breathing? What would you do if these signs and symptoms occurred while you were caring for Mr. Roberson?
- Who is responsible for suctioning Mr. Roberson? What responsibility would you have if he needs to be suctioned?

CAREER PREPARATIONS

Fill-in-the-Blanks

Fill in the word or phrase that best completes the sentence or answers the question.

1 What happens if the IV needle or catheter is moved and comes out of the vein? ______________________

2 Why is nasal care given frequently when the person is receiving oxygen or has a nasogastric tube in place? ______________________

3 What should you report to the nurse when caring for a person who needs suctioning?

a ______________________

b ______________________

c ______________________

4 Why are gloves worn when collecting a sputum specimen? ______________________

____

5 Why is it important to explain the procedure and get the person's permission before performing a vaginal irrigation? ______________________

____

____

Choose the Correct Answer

Choose the answer that will answer or complete the question and circle the letter next to it.

6 Which of these procedures may be done by a nursing assistant?

- **a** Administering oxygen therapy
- **b** Suctioning
- **c** Collecting a sputum specimen
- **d** Adjusting IV flow rate

7 Why can a portable IV pump be rolled along when the person is ambulating?

- **a** It runs on batteries when it is disconnected from the wall socket for short periods of time.
- **b** It has a very long cord that allows it to move around freely.
- **c** It can be turned off while the person is ambulating.
- **d** The IV is stopped with the clamp during ambulation.

8 Which of these statements is true about administering oxygen with a face mask?

- **a** It irritates the nose and throat.
- **b** It may cause feelings of suffocation.
- **c** The person may eat and drink while it is in place.
- **d** Smoking is allowed in the room where the person is sitting.

9 When is the best time to collect a sputum specimen?

- **a** At mealtime
- **b** Early in the morning
- **c** At bedtime
- **d** After using mouthwash

Matching

Match the job description with the jobs listed.

- **a** Phlebotomist
- **b** Pharmacy clerk
- **c** EKG (ECG) technician

10 ______ Takes electrocardiograms to test the function of the heart

11 ______ Draws blood from persons for laboratory studies

12 ______ Orders and stocks supplies, labels drugs, and cleans equipment and work areas in the pharmacy

Word Jumbler

Unscramble the terms and use the circled letters to make a word that completes the sentence.

13 **a** C Y P E T A N A H

◯ _ _ _ _ _ _ _ _

b S P E D Y N A

_ _ _ _ ◯ _ _

c G L I N G U R G

_ ◯ _ _ _ ◯ _ ◯

d L E S T E R S E S N S S

_ _ _ _ _ _ _ _ _ _ _ ◯

e N I A S S O C Y

◯ _ _ _ ◯ _ ◯ _

f These are indications that the patient or resident needs upper airway

_ _ _ _ _ _ _ _ _ _

Labeling

14 What are the two parts of the IV tubing indicated in Figure 24-1?

a ______________________________

b ______________________________

15 What information can you see and report to the nurse by looking at "a"?

____

16 Who is responsible for changing the position of "b"? ______________

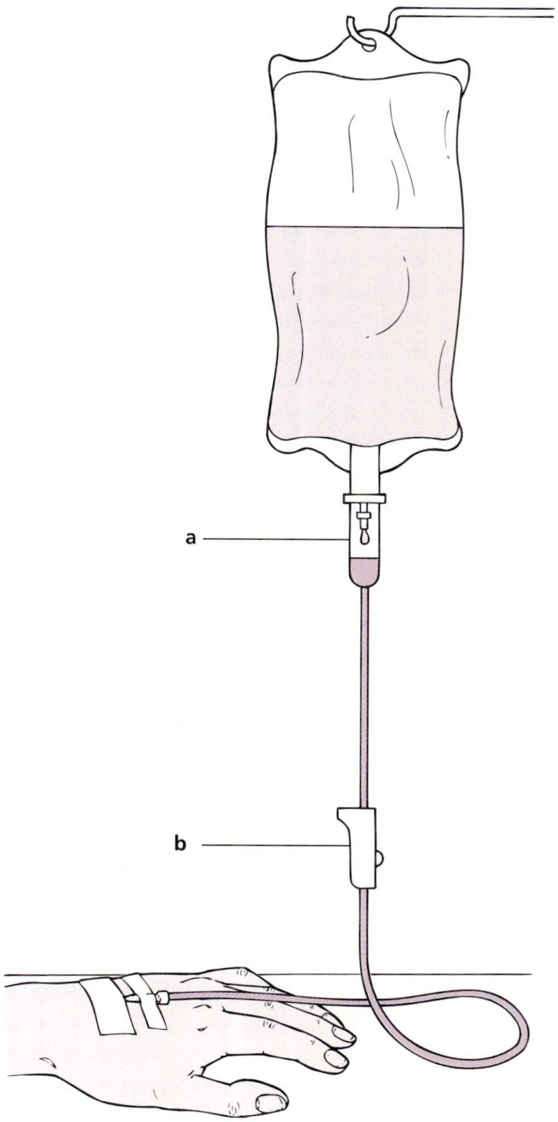

Fig. 24-1 *Intravenous therapy.*

25 The Person Having Surgery

PERSONAL EXPLORATIONS

1 Use the case study to answer the questions about caring for a person before surgery.

CASE STUDY: Herbert Long is scheduled to have bowel surgery this afternoon. You are assigned to care for him in the morning. The nurse tells you he is NPO and will need enemas till clear. You are assigned to do a shave prep before Mr. Long goes to the operating room.

- Why will Mr. Long need to take a bath and shampoo his hair during the morning?
- What will you tell Mr. Long when he asks you for a cup of coffee?
- How will you secure Mr. Long's wedding band to his finger before he goes to surgery?
- What part of his body will you shave for the shave prep? What is the purpose of the shave prep?
- How many enemas will be needed to prepare Mr. Long for surgery? What type of solution will be used? How much solution will be given with each enema?
- After Mr. Long leaves for the operating room, what will you do to prepare his room for his return?

2 Role play the following situation with a classmate. Take turns being the nursing assistant and the nurse.

SITUATION: While you are caring for Mr. Long, the nurse asks you to get his surgical permit signed. She tells you she has already discussed the surgery with Mr. Long, but she does not have time to go to his room with the permit. The nurse states that she will sign as the witness when you bring the permit to her. Consider these questions to guide your thinking.

- What would you say to the nurse when asked to get the permit signed?
- What could happen if you do as the nurse asks?
- Since she is planning to sign the permit, could you do as she asks? Why or why not?
- What would you do if the nurse got angry with you because you questioned the order?

CAREER PREPARATIONS

Matching

Match the descriptions or examples given with the correct type of surgery.

a Elective surgery
b Emergency surgery
c Major surgery
d Minor surgery
e Urgent surgery

1 ______ Done immediately to save the person's life

2 ______ Done when the coronary arteries are blocked

3 ______ Complex surgery that has many risks and complications

4 ______ Done for the person's well-being

5 ______ Type of surgery needed after an accident

6 ______ Must be done soon to prevent further damage or disease

7 ______ Cosmetic surgery

8 ______ Simple surgery with few risks or complications

Determine when each of these events occurs during the surgical process.

a Preoperatively
b Postoperatively

9 ______ Chest x-ray, CBC, and EKG

10 ______ Vital signs are measured every 15 minutes for the first hour

11 ______ Coughing and deep-breathing exercises as ordered

12 ______ Preoperative teaching

13 ______ Antiembolic stockings are applied

14 ______ Operative permit signed

Fill-in-the-Blanks

Fill in the word or phrase that best completes the sentence or answers the question.

15 Who is responsible for telling the person and family about the need for surgery? ______________________________

16 What should you do if the person or family asks you the results of the surgery? ______________________________

17 What does NPO mean? ______________________________

18 Why are makeup and nail polish removed before surgery? ______________________________

____

19 What type of anesthesia produces loss of sensation in a large area of the body? ______________________________

20 What should you do if you are taking postoperative vital signs and find the pulse is 120 beats per minute? ______________________________

21 Why is the person repositioned every 1 to 2 hours after surgery? ______________________________

____

22 Why are leg exercises important postoperatively? ______________________________

____

23 How do elastic stockings help to prevent the development of blood clots (thrombi)? ______________________________

24 What is wound dehiscence? ______________________________

25 What five complications may be prevented by having the person ambulate soon after surgery?

a ______________________________

b ______________________________

c ______________________________

d ______________________________

e ______________________________

26 Why is it important to report that a person has voided 6 hours after surgery?

____

Choose the Correct Answer

Circle the letter next to the statement that best completes the sentence or answers the question.

27 Why is a catheter ordered for some surgeries?

- **a** To keep the bladder empty during surgery
- **b** To prevent bladder infections postoperatively
- **c** To prevent incontinence
- **d** To keep the person from getting out of bed to go to the bathroom

28 What type of enema is given to clear the colon of feces?

- **a** Commercial enema
- **b** Oil-retention enema
- **c** Suppositories
- **d** Cleansing enema

29 Why should you wear gloves when you are doing a shave prep?

- **a** To protect the person against bacteria from your skin
- **b** To protect you against bloodborne pathogens
- **c** To keep the skin sterile
- **d** To protect your hands against irritating substances in the soap used to shave

30 When you are assigned to give coughing and deep-breathing exercises, which of these actions would be *incorrect?*

- **a** Place the person in semi-Fowler's position.
- **b** Instruct the person to take shallow breaths.
- **c** Tell the person to support the surgical wound with a small pillow.
- **d** Tell the person to cough strongly twice.

31 What movement does the person make with the foot when you instruct him/her to dorsiflex the foot?

- **a** Makes circles with the toes
- **b** Points the toes downward toward the foot of the bed
- **c** Points the toes upward as in a standing position
- **d** Turns the foot from side to side

32 Why are the fingers or toes exposed when an elastic bandage is applied?

- **a** To prevent skin breakdown
- **b** To allow movement of the fingers and toes
- **c** To allow the circulation to be checked
- **d** To allow the person to use the extremity

26 Rehabilitation and Restorative Care

PERSONAL EXPLORATIONS

1 Role play the situation with a classmate. Take turns being the nursing assistant and the person with the disability. Use your nondominant hand to attempt the activities she must do.

SITUATION: Mary Leeds, 62, had a cerebrovascular accident last month. She has hemiparesis on her dominant side and has been admitted to a rehabilitation unit to relearn activities of daily living (ADLs). She is practicing eating by using a spoon to place fluids and food in her mouth. She is also learning to button clothing. Consider these questions about how you felt when you were "Ms. Leeds."

- How well could you hold the spoon with your nondominant hand? What problems did you having controlling the spoon?
- How rapidly could you eat? What type of food was easier to eat?
- How well were you able to button your clothing? What techniques did you find that made you more successful?
- How did this experience make you feel? How will it affect the way you interact with persons who have similar disabilities?

2 With your instructor's permission, borrow a wheelchair from your school to use for 1 or 2 hours. Have a classmate push you around in the chair in a grocery store or mall. You must stay in the chair for the entire time to experience the feelings of a person who must use a wheelchair. Use a handicap-equipped bathroom during this experience.

- How comfortable was the wheelchair? Did you use any special padding or cushion in the seat?
- What difficulties were encountered moving about? Doorways? Steps? Aisles? Crowds? How did you deal with any difficulties?
- How accessible was the handicap-equipped bathroom? How much room was available for you to transfer from the wheelchair to the toilet?
- How did other people treat you? How many spoke to you? How many directed conversations to your classmate and avoided you?
- How did this experience make you feel? How will it affect the way you interact with a person in a wheelchair?

CAREER PREPARATIONS

Matching

Match the following words with the correct definitions.

a Activities of daily living
b Prosthesis
c Rehabilitation
d Aphasia
e Dysphagia

1 ______ Difficulty swallowing

2 ______ Process of restoring a person to the highest possible level of function

3 ______ Difficulty speaking

4 ______ Self-care activities performed to remain independent

5 ______ Artificial replacement for a missing body part

Word Jumbler

6 Unscramble the terms and use the circled letters to make a word that completes the sentence.

a R O C D O T

_ _ _ _ ◯ _

b S U R N E

◯ _ _ _ ◯

c A S I S T H E P R T

_ _ _ ◯ _ ◯ _ _ _ ◯

d The most important member of the health care team is the _ _ _ _ _ _ receiving care.

Fill-in-the-Blanks

Fill in the word or phrase that best completes the sentence or answers the question.

7 In what areas will rehabilitation help restore the person to the highest level of function?

a ______________________________

b ______________________________

c ______________________________

d ______________________________

8 Why is good skin care important in rehabilitation? ______________________________

____

9 What are four ways to prevent contractures during rehabilitation?

a ______________________________

b ______________________________

c ______________________________

d ______________________________

10 What are five common activities of daily living that are frequently relearned in rehabilitation?

a ______________________________

b ______________________________

c ______________________________

d ______________________________

e ______________________________

11 How can an electric toothbrush help a person with a disability become more independent? ______________________________

____

12 What is the goal of using a prosthesis? ______________________________

____

13 Why may a person with a disability feel depressed, angry, or hostile?

____

14 What types of therapy are required as part of rehabilitation according to OBRA?

a ______________________________

b ______________________________

c ______________________________

15 How does including the person as a member of the rehabilitation team improve his/her quality of life? ______________________________

____

Choose the Correct Answer

Circle the letter next to the statement that best completes the sentence or answers the question.

16 What is a major goal of rehabilitation?

- **a** To restore the person completely to health
- **b** To restore the person to a normal life
- **c** To restore the ability to perform activities of daily living
- **d** To restore the ability to return to the job performed before the disability occurred

17 Which of the following is a prosthesis?

- **a** Artificial leg
- **b** Eyeglasses
- **c** Leg brace
- **d** Hearing aid

18 How is feeding done if the person will never be able to swallow again?

- **a** Giving only liquids by mouth
- **b** Teaching special exercises to restore swallowing
- **c** Feeding through a nasogastric tube
- **d** Feeding through a gastrostomy tube

19 Which of these is *not* a responsibility of a nursing assistant in rehabilitation?

- **a** To perform range-of-motion exercises as instructed
- **b** To correct the person firmly when exercises are not done correctly
- **c** To give praise when even a little progress is made
- **d** To practice the task the person must perform
- **e** To encourage the person to perform activities of daily living as much as possible

True or False

Read each statement and circle T if it is true, and F if it is false. If the statement is false, in the space beneath the statement, change the words to make the statement true.

20 T F A disability does not affect a person's psychological well-being. It is only a physical problem.

____

21 T F Rehabilitation begins by preventing complications.

____

22 T F In the early stages of rehabilitation, a person may expect the therapy to correct the disability.

____

23 T F Only health care workers are members of the rehabilitation team.

____

24 T F When the health care team sets goals for the person, they can never be changed.

____

25 Fill in the 13 spokes of the wheel in Figure 26-1 with the members of the rehabilitation team.

Diagram

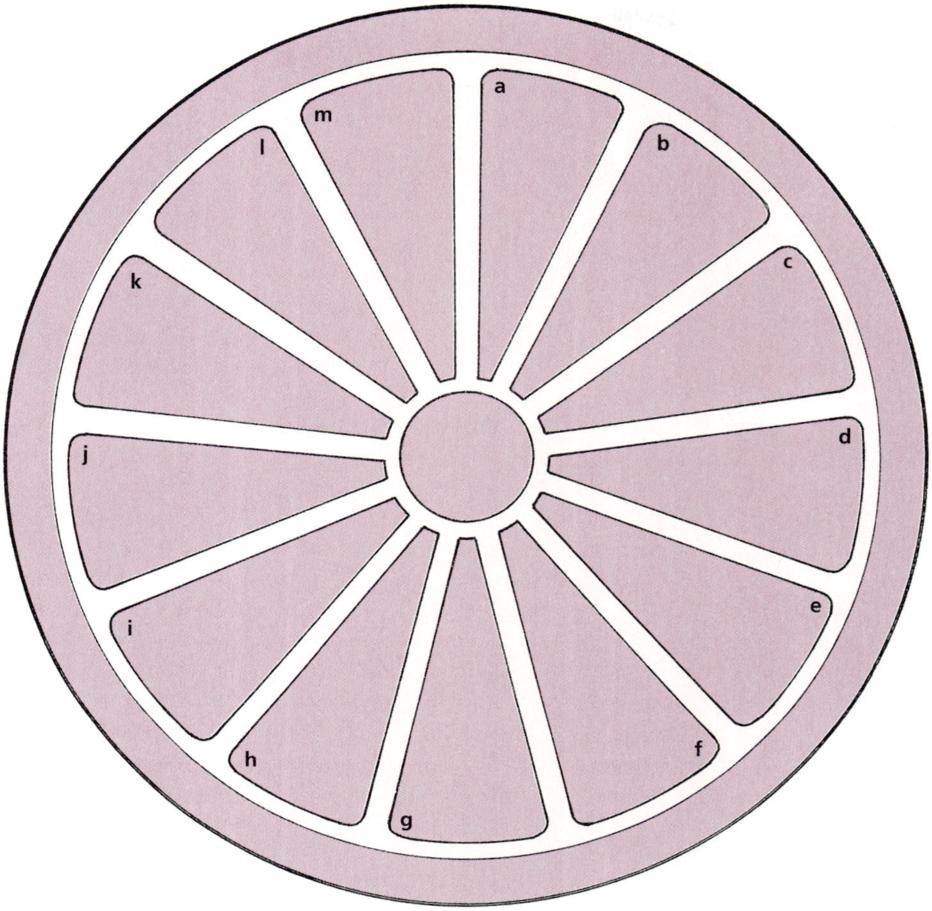

Fig. 26-1 *Rehabilitation team wheel.*

21 Persons with Hearing and Vision Problems

PERSONAL EXPLORATIONS

1 Cover your ears so that you cannot hear clearly. Use one of these methods or one that you devise.

- Commercial earplugs
- Cotton plugs in ears
- Cover ears with earmuffs or similar devices

Keep your ears covered and hearing muffled for at least 1 hour as you go about your daily activities. (A wise student will *not* wear earplugs during class time!) Answer the following questions about the experience.

- How did you find yourself compensating for the hearing loss? Turning up the TV or radio? Asking others to write out information? Staying away from others? Getting angry or frustrated?
- When you could not understand someone, what did you do? Ask them to repeat? Ask them to speak louder? Answer even if you were unsure of what was said? Not respond at all?
- If you answered when unsure, what was your response? Did you tend to agree or disagree with the speaker? Why?
- What methods listed in the chapter were helpful? What other methods did you use to understand what was being said? Watching the speaker? Cupping your hand around ears?
- How will this experience assist you when you care for a person with a hearing loss?

2 Cover your eyes with a blindfold so you cannot see. Keep the blindfold on for at least 1 hour as you go about your normal activities. Have someone act as a guide during this time. In addition to your normal activities, include the activities listed:

- Go outside with your guide and cross a street;
- Visit a store or restaurant with your guide;
- Eat a simple snack or meal;
- Go to the toilet, wash your hands, and comb your hair; and
- Have your guide take you to a public area, place you in a chair or on a bench, and leave you alone for 5 to10 minutes.

NOTE: You may wish to carry out this exercise using the blindfold and using this alternate method. If you wear glasses, cover the lenses with a heavy coating of petroleum jelly. This will simulate the vision experienced by a person with cataracts. Answer the questions for both experiences.

- How did you feel when you were unable to see what was going on around you? What noises or other sensory stimulants did you notice?
- When you were crossing the street, how did you feel? Safe? Frightened?
- When you were in a public area, what did you notice? How did you feel? How did others respond to you?
- How comfortable did you feel about eating when you could not see the food? How were you able to locate the food? What problems did you have?
- How did you manage in the bathroom? Were you able to find the equipment you needed? How competent did you feel about carrying out hand washing and grooming without seeing?
- What were your feelings when left alone in a public area for 5 to10 minutes? How long did it seem to be before your guide returned? What concerns did you have? Safety? Fear of injury? Desertion?
- How will this experience assist you when caring for a person with a vision loss?

3 Organize a group discussion with your classmates who have carried out the exercises to simulate vision and hearing problems. Answer these questions.

- Which disability did you find the most difficult to tolerate? Why?
- If you had to live with one of these disabilities, which one would you choose? Why?
- What happened during these exercises that surprised you about being unable to see or hear? How does this discovery change your attitude about the disabilities?

CAREER PREPARATIONS

Matching

Match the terms related to hearing and vision problems with the correct definition.

a Otitis media
b Tinnitus
c Vertigo
d Braille

1 ______ Dizziness

2 ______ Ringing in the ears

3 ______ Method of writing using raised dots

4 ______ Infection of the middle ear

Decoding Braille

5 Using the Braille alphabet, decode the sentence in Figure 27-1. The larger dots represent the raised dots.

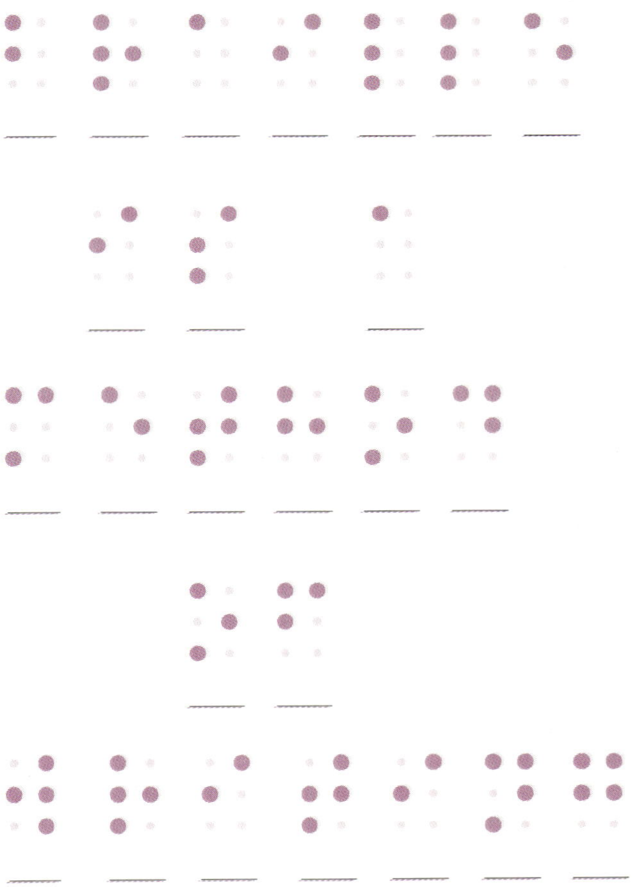

Fig. 27-1 *Decoding Braille.*

Fill-in-the-Blanks

Fill in the word or phrase that best completes the sentence or answers the question.

6 What may happen if an infant has a hearing impairment? ______________________

____

7 Why do persons with a hearing loss often become suspicious of others?

____

8 Why is it important for a hearing impaired person to see you when you are speaking to them? ______________________

9 What should you do to get the attention of a hearing impaired person?

____

10 Why are safety measures used with a blind person also used with a person who has an eye shield after cataract surgery? ______________________

____

11 What should be reported to the nurse immediately if it occurs to a person who has had cataract surgery? ______________________

____

12 What is the first action you should do when you enter the room of a blind person? ______________________

Riddles

Read the statements and solve the riddles.

13 What disease am I? ______________________

- In this disease I increase the pressure within the eye.
- I may have a gradual or sudden onset.
- My signs and symptoms include tunnel vision, blurred vision, and blue-green halos around lights.
- With a sudden onset, I cause severe eye pain, nausea, and vomiting.

14 What disease am I? ______________________

- I involve increased fluid in the inner ear.
- My symptoms are vertigo, tinnitus, and hearing loss.

15 What disorder am I? ______________________

- In this disorder I cause the lens to become opaque.
- I cause a gradual blurring and dimming of vision.
- I can occur in one or both eyes.
- Aging is my most common cause.

Choose the Correct Answer

Circle the letter next to the statement that best completes the sentence or answers the question.

16 Which disorder may cause vertigo?

- **a** Glaucoma
- **b** Otitis media
- **c** Meniere's disease
- **d** Cataracts

17 Which of these signs may indicate a person has a hearing impairment? (Circle *all* the correct answers.)

- **a** Speaking very softly
- **b** Asking for words to be repeated
- **c** Pronouncing words very clearly
- **d** Leaning forward to hear
- **e** Answering questions inappropriately
- **f** Cupping the better ear toward the speaker

18 What disease is a major cause of blindness?

- **a** Cataracts
- **b** Glaucoma
- **c** Vertigo
- **d** Otitis media

19 Which of these is *not* a responsibility of a nursing assistant?

- **a** To check the battery position in a hearing aid
- **b** To clean eyeglasses with warm water
- **c** To insert contact lenses
- **d** To speak when entering the room of a blind person

28 Common Health Problems

PERSONAL EXPLORATIONS

1 Many people have had a fracture at some time during their life. If you have had a broken bone, answer the questions based on your experience.

- How did it feel? Did you know it was broken right away or several hours or days later? How much pain did you have?
- What treatment was done? A cast? Surgery? Pins, plates, screws, traction?
- What effect did the fracture have on your day-to-day activities? Work? Schooling? Leisure activities?
- What accommodations were needed to carry out ADLs? Toileting? Bathing? Dressing?
- How was mobility affected? Ambulation? Sitting in a car? Driving a car?
- What discomfort or pain did you experience during the healing process? With the cast? With any surgical incision?
- What long-range problems occurred because of this injury? Periodic pain? Limited mobility?

2 If you have never had a fracture, try this experiment to get a small sample of how the fracture may interfere with your life. Make an immobilizer for your leg. Use one of the methods suggested or devise your own immobilizer.

- Use four pieces of sturdy cardboard that are long enough to reach from the ankle to midthigh. Place on the front, back, and sides of the leg.
- Use several thicknesses of newspaper or magazines and wrap around the leg to immobilize the knee and ankle.
- Secure the immobilizer with an elastic bandage or soft cloth strips.

After the immobilizer is in place, leave it on for 1 to 2 hours and go about your normal routine. Answer the questions about what you experienced.

- How much did the "cast" interfere with your routine?
- What problems occurred because of the "cast"?
- How did you feel when you were in the "cast"? Awkward? As if everyone was looking at you?

3 Try these experiments to understand how these diseases affect the body or the person.

- Osteoporosis. Fold a piece of standard 8-inch by 10-inch paper in half, in half again, and in half a third time. (It will now be about 1 inch by 10 inches.) Now try to break it in half; pull it from either end to break it. What happens? Unfold the paper once and cut several holes along the edges. If necessary, unfold it again to carry out this step. This will make the paper porous, much like bone becomes with osteoporosis. Refold the paper to the original 1-inch by 10-inch size and attempt to break it in half or pull it apart from the ends. What happens this time?
- Coronary artery disease. Use a straw to drink water. Now, put small pieces of paper towel into the end of the straw and try to drink through it. What happens? Keep adding more paper towel to the straw and try to draw fluid through the straw. How does this relate to coronary artery disease?

4 Consider the following situation. Answer the questions about how you would respond to this information.

SITUATION: Your doctor has just told you that you have cancer and will probably only live 6 months.

- How do you think you would react immediately? After a few days?
- What changes would you make in your life? Why?
- What would be your biggest concern? Why?
- What would you want to do with the time you had? With whom would you want to spend the time?
- With whom would you share the information about your diagnosis?
- How would you respond to others who offered sympathy or assistance? Why would you respond in this way?
- How would you like others to treat you at this time? Why?

CAREER PREPARATIONS

Choose the Correct Answer

Circle the letter next to the statement that best completes the sentence or answers the question.

1 Which of these methods is used to take the medication used for angina?

a Inhalation
b Swallowing it with water
c Placing it under the tongue
d Injection

2 Which of these body parts are most commonly affected by osteoarthritis?

a Spine, hips, and knees
b Heart and lungs
c Fingers and hands
d Connective tissue

3 Which of these should be done when a new cast is drying?

a Place the cast on a hard surface.
b Cover it to retain heat.
c Use your palms to move and position the cast.
d Use narrow objects to scratch areas of irritation under the cast.

4 Which of the following should be avoided by a person with osteoporosis?

a Bed rest
b Walking
c Exercise
d A diet rich in calcium

5 Which of these symptoms are likely to be present in a person with Parkinson's disease?

a Weakness and tremors on one side of the body
b Tremors and shuffling gait
c Aphasia and dysphagia
d Mental confusion and dementia

6 Which of these actions would be *incorrect* when caring for a person in traction?

a Not adding weights to the traction
b Performing range-of-motion exercises to uninvolved body parts
c Removing the weights when giving care
d Having the person use the trapeze to raise his/her body off the bed

7 If you are caring for a person who has renal calculi, what should you do with the urine?

a Measure it to keep a record of output.
b Strain it to find stones.
c Send it to the lab for tests.
d Test it for the presence of sugar.

Matching

Match the disease listed with the correct definition or symptom described.

a Parkinson's disease
b Multiple sclerosis
c Osteoporosis
d Osteoarthritis
e Cerebrovascular accident

8 ______ Myelin sheath is destroyed.

9 ______ Bones become porous and brittle.

10 ______ Blood supply to the brain is suddenly interrupted.

11 ______ Person has masklike expression.

12 ______ Smooth surfaces of the joints break down.

Match the type of aphasia with the correct definitions.

a Aphasia
b Expressive aphasia
c Expressive-receptive aphasia
d Receptive aphasia

13 ______ Difficulty sending out thoughts and receiving information

14 ______ Inability to speak

15 ______ Difficulty receiving information

16 ______ Difficulty sending out thoughts

Riddles

Read the statements and solve the riddles.

17 What disease am I? ______________________

My signs and symptoms include:

- the alveoli becoming enlarged;
- walls of the alveoli becoming less elastic;
- some air remaining trapped in the alveoli during expiration; and
- shortness of breath and "smoker's cough."

18 What disease am I? ______________________

My signs and symptoms include:

- blurred or double vision;
- tremors;
- numbness and tingling;
- weakness;
- dizziness;
- urinary incontinence;
- anal incontinence; and
- incoordination.

19 What disease am I? ______________________

My signs and symptoms include:

- dizziness;
- ringing in the ears;
- headache;
- nausea and vomiting;
- memory loss; and
- weakness on one side of the body.

20 What disease am I? ______________________

My signs and symptoms include:

- masklike facial expression;
- tremors;
- pill-rolling movements of the fingers;
- shuffling gait;
- stooped posture;
- stiff muscles;
- slow movements;
- slurred or monotone speech; and
- drooling.

Fill-in-the-Blanks

Fill in the word or phrase that best completes the sentence or answers the question.

21 What are the seven early warning signs of cancer?

a C ____

b A ____

c U ____

d T ____

e I ____

f O ____

g N ____

22 What are the two types of arthritis? What are the age groups most commonly affected by each type?

a ____

b ____

23 What are the goals in treating rheumatoid arthritis?

a ____

b ____

c ____

24 What are the reasons for doing arthroplasty surgery?

a ____

b ____

25 These are the signs and symptoms to report if they occur to a person with a cast. What could be occurring to cause each of the symptoms?

a Pain ______________________

b Swelling/tight cast ______________________

c Pale skin ______________________

d Cyanosis ______________________

e Odor ______________________

f Inability to move toes or fingers ______________________

g Numbness ______________________

h Temperature changes ______________________

i Drainage on or under the cast ______________________

j Chills, fever, nausea, vomiting ______________________

26 What are the causes of osteoporosis?

a ______________________

b ______________________

c ______________________

d ______________________

27 What is it called when a person complains of pain in an amputated limb?

____

28 Why is a person who has had a stroke placed in a lateral position? ________

____

29 What four respiratory disorders are included in chronic obstructive pulmonary disease (COPD)?

a ______________________

b ______________________

c ______________________

d ______________________

30 Why would the doctor order "force fluids" for a person who has pneumonia?

____

31 Why is it important for a person with angina to have nitroglycerin available at all times? ______________________

32 When you care for a person with congestive heart failure (CHF), what are two things you may need to measure each day?

a ______________________

b ______________________

33 If a person has a myocardial infarction (heart attack), where could pain be felt in addition to the left chest area?

a ______

b ______

c ______

34 What are signs and symptoms of diabetes mellitus?

a ______

b ______

c ______

d ______

35 Why is a casted extremity elevated on pillows? ______

36 When a person has hip surgery, how is the affected leg positioned? Adducted or abducted? ______

37 In the position chosen in question 36, are the legs kept close together or spread apart? ______

38 What is the purpose of trochanter rolls? ______

39 The following are risk factors for hypertension. How are each of these factors a risk?

a Age ______

b Sex ______

c Race ______

d Family ______

e Weight ______

f Stress ______

g Cigarette smoking ______

h Salt intake ______

i Alcohol ______

j Exercise ______

k Atherosclerosis ______

40 Why should you wear a mask when caring for a person with tuberculosis?

______

41 A urinary tract infection is a common nosocomial infection. Where is a nosocomial infection acquired? ______

42 If you are caring for a person in renal failure, what would you report immediately to the nurse about the urine output? ______

43 What types of vehicles can transmit communicable diseases when ingested?

______

44 By what route is hepatitis type A usually spread? ____________________

45 By what route is hepatitis type B usually spread? ____________________

46 Why do persons with AIDS often develop other diseases? ____________________

Labeling

47 In Figure 28-1, identify the areas where the pain of angina pectoris is felt.

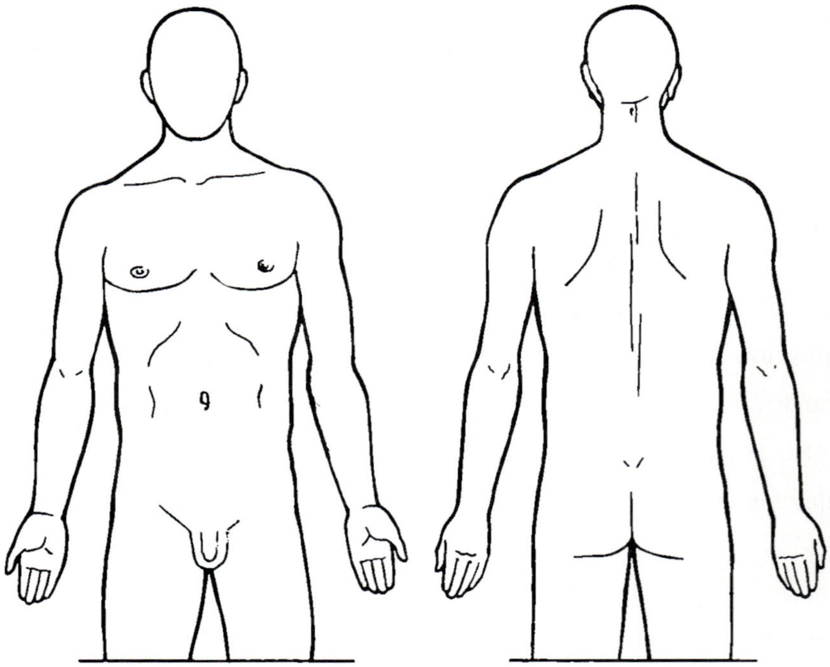

Fig. 28-1 *Angina pectoris.*

48 In Figure 28-2, identify where the fatty deposits can collect on the walls of the arteries in atherosclerosis.

Fig. 28-2 *Atherosclerosis.*

Word Jumbler

Fill in the blanks with a word that corresponds to the word beside it. Identify the terms and use the circled letters to make a word that completes the sentence.

49 **a** Frequent thirst

_ _ _ _ ◯ _ _ _ _ _

b Frequent urination

_ _ _ _ _ _ ◯ _

c Sugar in the urine

_ _ _ _ _ ◯ _ _ _ _

d Increased hunger

_ _ _ _ _ _ ◯ _ _ _

e Increased sweating

_ _ _ _ _ _ _ ◯ _ _ _

f Loss of vision caused by damage to the retina

◯ _ _ _ _ _ _ _ _

g The body system that secretes hormones

◯ _ _ _ _ _ _ _ _

h Family history of a disease

_ _ _ _ _ ◯ _

i The disease described is _ _ _ _ _ _ _ _

29

Mental Health Problems

PERSONAL EXPLORATIONS

1 Try this experiment with a group of classmates. Make up labels with various roles for "staff members" and "mentally ill." A list is provided, but you may add or subtract according to the size of your group. Make sure that the group includes a mixture of people with mental health problems and staff or visitors.

Doctor	A person with bipolar disorder
Nurse	A person with delusions of grandeur
Visitor	A person with obsessive-compulsive disorder
Nursing assistant	A person with schizophrenia with paranoia
Recreational therapist	A person with hallucinations
Dietician	A person with anorexia nervosa

Attach a label to each person so that they cannot read it. (It may be placed on the back or the forehead.) Have everyone move about the group and talk to each other based on how the person thinks he/she should approach the person with a certain "label." Continue the experiment for about 15 minutes and then use the questions to guide a group discussion.

- How did you feel talking to a person with a mental health disorder?
- How were the people with a mental health disorder approached? How quickly were the "mentally ill" able to sense that this was their label? What cues did they receive from others?
- How quickly did "staff members" recognize the label they had? What cues did they receive from others?

- In what ways did the approach of others cause people to respond in a way expected? Did the people with mental health problems show signs of the illness based on the reaction of others?
- What did the group learn about approaching a person with a mental health problem?

2 Consider this situation and answer the questions concerning how you would feel about caring for a person with a mental health problem.

SITUATION: Marion Cross, 65, is a patient in an acute care hospital with a diagnosis of pneumonia. The nurse tells you Mrs. Cross has a history of schizophrenia. You are assigned to provide AM care for Mrs. Cross.

- How would you approach Mrs. Cross when you enter her room? How would your knowledge about her mental health problem affect your initial contact with her?
- What would you do if Mrs. Cross told you she sees an elephant in the room? What would you say to her?
- How would you react if Mrs. Cross told you that she owns Disney World and goes there free anytime she wants? How would you respond?
- How would you provide good oral hygiene if Mrs. Cross refuses to cooperate because she is sure the staff is trying to poison her? What could you try that might be helpful?
- What would you do if Mrs. Cross curls up in a tight ball and refuses to talk or cooperate during AM care? What could you do to maintain her hygiene?
- How would you feel about caring for a person with abnormal behavior? Why?

CAREER PREPARATIONS

Mental Health

Crossword

ACROSS

4. Seeing, hearing, or feeling something that is not real
5. Uncontrolled performance of an act
8. Part of the personality at the unconscious level; concerned with pleasure
9. Intense and sudden feeling of fear, anxiety, terror, or dread
11. Part of the personality concerned with what is right and wrong
13. False belief
14. Fear, panic, or dread

DOWN

1. False beliefs and suspicion about a person or situation
2. Memory, past experiences, and thoughts of which the person is not aware
3. Aware of the environment and experiences; person knows what is happening
6. Person does not view or interpet reality correctly
7. Persistent thought or idea
10. Feelings and emotions
12. Part of the personality dealing with reality; deals with problem solving, thoughts, and feelings

Fill-in-the-Blanks

Fill in the word or phrase that best completes the sentence or answers the question.

1 What part of the personality is concerned with morals and values? ________

____

2 What part of the personality is involved with thoughts, feelings, reasons, good sense, and problem solving? ____________________

3 At what level of awareness does the id operate? ____________________

4 If a person believes he/she is president of the United States, what type of false belief is present? ______________________

5 If a person sits for hours without moving, speaking, or responding, what type of psychosis is present? ______________________

6 What are the two extremes of a bipolar disorder? ______________________

7 What is the name of the disorder if a person is afraid of dirt or contamination? ______________________

Riddles

Read the statements and solve the riddles.

8 What am I? ______________________

- I start at birth.
- I am influenced by many factors such as genes, culture, environment, parenting, and social skills.
- I am affected by Maslow's theory of basic needs.
- I am the set of attitudes, values, behaviors, and characteristics of a particular person.

9 What mental health disorder am I? ______________________

My signs and symptoms include:

- disturbed thinking and behavior;
- delusions and hallucinations;
- difficulty relating to others and the world; and
- regressing.

10 What mental health disorder am I? ______________________

My signs and symptoms include:

- having vague, uneasy feelings;
- feeling a sense of danger or harm;
- occurring in response to stress;
- being present in all mental health disorders; and
- being unaware of source of uneasy feeling.

11 What am I? ______________________

- I cause extreme mood swings.
- At times I cause one to feel very sad, lonely, worthless.
- A person having me may consider suicide.
- A person having me may not take time to eat or drink.
- I cause one to have exaggerated beliefs about one's importance.

12 What mental health disorder am I? ______________________

My signs and symptoms include:

- a hostility and lack of loyalty to any person or group;
- a blaming of others for actions and behaviors;
- a lack of consideration for the rights of others;
- an absence of feelings of guilt; and
- a lack of learning from past experiences or punishments.

Choose the Correct Answer

Circle the letter next to the statement that best completes the sentence or answers the question.

13 Which of these may cause mental health disorders? (Circle *all* of the correct answers.)

a Inability to cope with stress
b Chemical imbalances in body
c Characteristics inherited from parents
d Drug abuse
e Social and cultural factors

14 Which of the following is an example of an unhealthy coping mechanism?

a Going for a walk
b Talking about a problem
c Exercising
d Chain smoking
e Having an extra piece of cake with a meal

15 Which of these would be present if a person has delusions of persecution?

a Seeing, hearing, or feeling something that is not there
b Not sleeping or taking time to tend to self-care needs
c Believing that one is mistreated, abused, or harassed
d Having poor judgment and lacking ethics and morals

16 When a young girl has anorexia nervosa, which of these behaviors is she likely to display?

a She diets even though she becomes emaciated.
b She withdraws from the world and shows no interest in others.
c She retreats to behaviors of a younger child.
d She has delusions or hallucinations.

17 When you are caring for a person with mental disorders, which of these is most important?

a Be able to assess vital signs correctly.
b Be careful of your body language.
c Give complete care well.
d Monitor intake and output accurately.

Matching

Match the term with the definition provided.

a Compensation
b Conversion
c Denial
d Displacement
e Identification
f Projection
g Rationalization
h Reaction
i Regression
j Repression

18 ______ When a person assumes the ideas, behaviors, and traits of another person

19 ______ To give some acceptable reason or excuse for one's own behavior or actions

20 ______ To make up for or substitute a strength for a weakness

21 ______ When an individual moves his/her behavior or emotions from one person, place, or thing to another person, place, or thing

22 ______ When an emotion is expressed or changed into a physical symptom

23 ______ Keeping unpleasant or painful thoughts or experiences from the conscious mind

24 ______ Blaming another person or object for one's own unacceptable behavior, emotions, ideas, or wishes

25 ______ When a person refuses to face or accept something that is unpleasant or threatening

26 ______ When a person acts in a way that is opposite to what he/she truly feels

27 ______ To retreat or move back to an earlier time or condition

28 All of the terms in the matching exercise are examples of unconscious reactions that block unpleasant or threatening feelings. These are called

______________________.

Match the level of anxiety experienced with the sign or symptom listed.

a Normal anxiety
b High anxiety

29 ______ Mary experiences "butterflies" in the stomach when asked to talk in front of a group.

30 ______ John does not go shopping at the mall because he has a fear of being in public or crowded places.

31 ______ Emily had difficulty sleeping the night before her recital.

32 ______ Michael washes his hands constantly because he is afraid of becoming ill.

33 ______ Susan experiences an intense and sudden feeling of terror for no obvious reason and is unable to move for several minutes.

30 Confusion and Dementia

PERSONAL EXPLORATIONS

1 Consider the situation and answer the questions about how you would feel.

SITUATION: Imagine you are in a strange country where people talk to you, but you do not understand what they are saying. They use strange tools to eat and you cannot figure out how to use them. They try to feed you food you do not recognize. Sometimes these people seem friendly and caring, but at other times they become angry because you are not doing what they ask you to do. You become frightened when they try to remove your clothes and take you in a room to shower you. You become frightened and upset because you do not know what will happen next. At times other strangers come to your room and bring gifts. They talk kindly to you, but you do not know them. They seem upset when you do not respond to their gifts and gestures. The doors and windows in this country are all locked, and you cannot find a way out so that you can go home.

- How does this situation relate to the information in this chapter?
- How would you react if you were the person in this situation? Why?
- What methods might you use to try to communicate with the person in this situation?
- Why would the person want to go home? What does "home" mean to him or her?
- How will this exercise help you when you care for a person who is confused?

2 Consider the situation and answer the questions about how you would care for a person who is confused.

SITUATION: You are assigned to care for Ronald Myers, 85, who has Alzheimer's disease. He often wanders from room to room and tries to open the outside doors. He frequently becomes agitated and restless, especially in the evening. Most of the time, Mr. Myers is unable to feed himself and is often incontinent. He keeps repeating "Help me, help me" all day long.

- How do you feel about caring for a confused person? Frightened? Angry? Impatient? How do you deal with your feelings so that you can give care to the person?
- At what stage of Alzheimer's disease is Mr. Myers? What signs and symptoms support your answer?
- Why would it be ineffective to remind Mr. Myers of the date and time during your shift? Why is this a good technique with some confused persons and not with others?
- Why does Mr. Myers become more agitated toward evening? What is this called?
- What methods could you use to make sure Mr. Myers receives the care needed to maintain good personal hygiene? How could you get him to cooperate or participate in his care?
- What parts of Mr. Myers' behavior would be most difficult for you to tolerate? What would you do if you found yourself becoming irritated and angry with Mr. Myers?
- What information in this chapter has helped you to understand persons like Mr. Myers better? How will this information help you to give better care to these persons and to maintain their quality of life?

CAREER PREPARATIONS

Choose the Correct Answer

Circle the letter next to the statement that best completes the sentence or answers the question.

1 What type of mental disorder occurs with AIDS?

a Acute confusion
b Dementia
c Pseudodementia
d Sundowning

2 What kind of environment is helpful when a person with Alzheimer's disease is agitated?

a Calm, quiet environment
b Complete silence or isolation
c A darkened room
d An area with music and people to distract the person

3 Which of these steps would *not* be helpful in caring for a confused person?

- **a** Call the person by name each time you have contact with him/her.
- **b** Keep clocks and calendars in the person's room.
- **c** Maintain a daily routine of activities.
- **d** Explain all of the day's planned activities in the morning.

4 What service is *not* offered by the Alzheimer's disease support group?

- **a** Advice and ideas about caring for the person with Alzheimer's disease
- **b** Assistance with financial needs
- **c** A place to share anger and frustration
- **d** Support and encouragement to family

5 When a person is confused, what food substance is thought to increase restlessness, confusion, and agitation?

- **a** Fats
- **b** Caffeine
- **c** Dairy products
- **d** Salt

Matching

Match the type of confusion with the characteristic described.

- **a** Acute confusion
- **b** Chronic confusion

6 ______ Occurs gradually with physical changes of aging

7 ______ Can occur postoperatively

8 ______ Usually is temporary

9 ______ May be caused by losses of hearing and sight

10 ______ Treatment is aimed at cause of confusion

11 ______ Gradual loss of ability to perform activities of daily living

12 ______ May be called dementia

Match the stage of Alzheimer's disease with the symptom described

- **1** Stage 1
- **2** Stage 2
- **3** Stage 3

13 ______ Restlessness increases during evening hours.

14 ______ Person cannot walk or sit.

15 ______ Person is less outgoing and less interested in things.

16 ______ Person forgets recent events.

17 ______ Person does not recognize family members.

18 ______ Person may say same thing over and over.

19 ______ Person cannot tell difference between hot and cold.

20 ______ Person becomes totally incontinent.

21 ______ Person is disoriented to time.

22 ______ Person cannot communicate.

23 ______ Person cannot follow directions.

Match the quality of life that can be met with the action described.

- **a** Privacy and confidentiality
- **b** Personal choice
- **c** Keep and use personal possessions
- **d** Freedom from abuse, mistreatment, neglect
- **e** Freedom from restraints
- **f** Activity

24 ______ Talking with the nurse about your frustration with a person

25 ______ Plan of care including safe, calm, quiet activity

26 ______ Giving the person and family a space where they can visit

27 ______ Allowing the person to move freely within the facility as long as he/she is not a danger to himself/herself

28 ______ Allowing the person to use a pillow from home

29 ______ Giving the person the choice to select an outfit to wear

Fill-in-the-Blanks

Fill in the word or phrase that best completes the sentence or answers the question.

30 What causes a progressive loss of brain cells with aging? ______________________

____

31 If a person is depressed, signs and symptoms of dementia may be present. What is this condition called? ______________________

32 In what age group does Alzheimer's disease commonly occur? ______________

33 Why is a person with Alzheimer's disease in danger of having accidents?

____

34 What are the reasons sundowning may occur in a person with Alzheimer's disease?

a ____

b ____

c ____

35 What response may occur if a person with Alzheimer's disease has too much stimuli at one time? ______________________

36 What are the reasons a family usually decides to place a person with Alzheimer's disease in a long-term care facility?

a ____

b ____

c ____

d ____

e ____

37 What is meant by the "sandwich generation"? ______________________

____

38 Why are locks placed at the top or bottom of a door to prevent wandering?

____

39 Why is it ineffective to argue or try to reason with a person with Alzheimer's disease? ______________________________________

Word Jumbler

Unscramble the terms and use the circled letters to make a word that completes the sentence.

40 **a** L A H C U L N A I T O N I

_ _ _ _ ◯ _ _ _ _ ◯ _ _ _

b L U S I L I N O S

_ _ _ _ _ _ _ ◯ _

c M E N D E T I A

_ ◯ _ ◯ _ _ _ ◯

d N U S N O W D G I N

_ _ _ _ _ _ _ _ _ ◯

e L U S I D E N O S

_ ◯ _ _ _ _ _ ◯ _

f N I C O G I V E T   M E N P A I M I R I T

_ ◯ _ _ _ _ _ _ _   _ ◯ _ _ _ ◯ _ _ _ _ _

g N O C S U F I O N

◯ _ _ _ _ _ _ _ _

h The dementia patient and family need much

_ _ _ _ _ _ _ _ _ _ _ _ _.

Puzzle

Complete the following statements and find the proper location in the puzzle for each word used.

1. Early in the day, activity and ____________________ should be encouraged.
2. Late in the day it is important to provide a calm, quiet ____________________.
3. Before performing any procedure provide a simple ____________________.
4. It is important to keep ____________________ levels low.
5. To calm and reassure the person, use ____________________.
6. The person may see, hear, or feel things that are not real. These are called ____________________.
7. Since judgment is poor, the person cannot tell what is safe or dangerous, and the caregiver must provide for the person's ____________________.
8. To promote communication, it is important to ____________________ ____________________.
9. It is important to keep activities and ____________________ simple.
10. To reduce the amount of time the person has to be involved in care measures, have the ____________________ ready for any procedure ahead of time.
11. Use the letters printed in the puzzle to spell a word related to this chapter.

_ _ _ _ _ _ _ _ _

I
N
O
O
U
C
N
F
S

31 Sexuality

PERSONAL EXPLORATIONS

1 Consider this situation about a sexually aggressive person and answer the questions about how you would respond.

SITUATION: John James, 72, has paraplegia because of an accident several years ago. His caregivers report that recently he has begun to make sexually suggestive remarks. While you are giving his AM care, he keeps touching you in private areas and makes frequent sexually suggestive remarks. The other nursing assistants tell you they just ignore him or joke around with him about the actions.

- What would you say to Mr. James when he touched you in private areas?
- How would you respond to his suggestive remarks?
- What would you say to your colleagues who suggest you ignore or joke with Mr. James?
- Has this type of situation ever occurred to you? How did you handle it then? What would you do differently after studying this chapter?

2 Consider this situation about caring for a person who is homosexual. Answer the questions about how you would respond.

SITUATION: Bobbie Freeman, 45, has had gallbladder surgery. While you assist her to ambulate, she begins to talk about her friend, Judy. She tells you that they have been lovers for 15 years.

- What would you say to a person who tells you she is homosexual?
- What effect would this information have on the care you provide for the person?
- Has this type of situation ever occurred when you were caring for a person? How did you respond? How would you respond after reading the information in this chapter?

CAREER PREPARATIONS

Word Jumbler

Unscramble the terms and use the circled letters to make a word that completes the sentence.

1 **a** A person who is attracted to people of the opposite sex

_ _ _ _ _ _ _ _ _ _ _ _ ◯

b A person who is attracted to both sexes

_ _ ◯ _ _ _ _ _

c A person who believes that he or she is really a member of the opposite sex

_ _ _ _ _ _ _ _ ◯ _ _

d A person who is attracted to a member of the same sex

_ _ _ _ _ _ _ ◯ _ _ _

e A person who becomes sexually excited by dressing in the clothes appropriate to the opposite sex

_ _ ◯ _ _ _ ◯ _ _ _ _ _

f These are examples of _ _ _ _ _ _ preference

Choose the Correct Answer

Circle the letter next to the statement that best completes the sentence or answers the question.

2 Which of these statements *does not* describe sexuality?

- **a** It involves the whole personality and the body.
- **b** It is influenced by social, cultural, and spiritual factors.
- **c** It is present from birth.
- **d** It is done for pleasure or to produce children.

3 Which of these statements is *true* about sexuality and the elderly?

- **a** After menopause, women are no longer interested in having sexual relations.
- **b** A man cannot have an erection as he gets older.
- **c** Sexual relationships are psychologically and physically important to the elderly.
- **d** Orgasm may be less intense and longer in duration.

4 What hormone is decreased in secretion as a man ages?

- **a** Testosterone
- **b** Estrogen
- **c** Progesterone
- **d** Gonads

5 Which of these methods is most effective in preventing the spread of sexually transmitted diseases?

- **a** Condoms
- **b** Birth control pills
- **c** Antibiotics
- **d** Spermicidal foam

Read each statement and decide if it promotes an individual's sexuality. If it does, circle P; if not, circle D. If the statement does not promote an individual's sexuality, in the space beneath the statement, change the words to make the statement promote an individual's sexuality.

6 P D Encouraging the person to wear a hospital gown at all times

____

7 P D Protecting the person's right to privacy

____

8 P D Encouraging an individual to get counseling if the person's sexual attitudes are different from yours

____

9 P D Knocking before entering a room

____

10 P D Allowing elderly persons the right to be sexual

____

11 P D Discouraging single elderly people from developing new relationships

____

12 P D Allowing couples in nursing facilities to share the same room

____

13 P D Discouraging women from shaving their underarms and legs

____

Fill-in-the-Blanks

Fill in the word or phrase that best completes the sentence or answers the question.

14 At what age are children aware of the sex of other children? ______________

____

15 When illness and injury occur, what kinds of sexual problems may develop?

____

16 What is the condition called when a man is unable to function sexually?

____

17 When menopause occurs, what two hormones are secreted in decreased amounts? ______________________________

18 What are ways elderly persons may express closeness and intimacy without having intercourse?

a ______________

b ______________

c ______________

d ______________

19 What are five ways you may deal with a person who is sexually aggressive toward you?

a ______________________________

b ______________________________

c ______________________________

d ______________________________

e ______________________________

20 How are sexually transmitted diseases spread?

a ______________________________

b ______________________________

c ______________________________

d ______________________________

Matching

Match the sign or symptom with the correct sexually transmitted disease.

a Genital herpes
b Gonorrhea
c Syphilis
d Venereal warts

21 ______ Painless chancre on penis

22 ______ Warts on penis, anus, or genitalia

23 ______ Vaginal discharge in females

24 ______ Damage to cardiovascular and central nervous systems

25 ______ Painful, fluid-filled sores on or near genitalia

26 ______ Burning on urination

27 ______ General fatigue, rash, and bone and joint pain

32 Caring for Mothers and Newborns

PERSONAL EXPLORATIONS

1 Imagine you are working for a home care agency and you are assigned to assist the family described. Answer the questions about how you would handle the situation.

SITUATION: Laura Collins, 18, had her first baby 1 week ago. She needs home care because she lives alone and had a cesarean section when the baby, Marc, was born. When you arrive, you notice several half-used bottles scattered around the living area. Laura rinses out a dirty bottle and pours new formula into it just as you arrive. Marc is lying on the couch with a bottle propped in his mouth. When Laura changes a diaper, you notice she does not clean the skin, the circumcision, or the cord. The diaper area is very reddened.

- What concerns do you have as soon as you observe Laura and Marc?
- What questions would you ask Laura? About herself? About feeding Marc? About preparing and storing formula? About diapering?
- What kind of information would you want to share with Laura about feeding? Formula handling?
- What would you want to show Laura about diapering and skin care? Circumcision care? Cord care?
- What would you do if Laura did not seem to accept your help? If she became angry with you?

2 Consider this situation and answer the questions about how you would try to help this mother and baby.

SITUATION: Your neighbor, Jenny, had a baby, Nicole, 4 days ago. She is trying to breastfeed, but she is becoming discouraged because she does not think Nicole is getting enough to eat. Jenny's mother told her that her milk is not strong enough, and the baby needs a bottle now and then. Jenny tells you Nicole only nurses for 5 or 10 minutes at a time, but then is hungry again in 2 hours. The nurse at the hospital told Jenny to drink 6 glasses of milk a day, but she does not like milk, so she has been drinking cola instead. Jenny tells you she is tired and has not been eating well since the baby was born.

- What would you do to decrease some of Jenny's concerns? What information could you share that would reassure her?
- What questions could you ask about her breastfeeding techniques? Hygiene? Positioning? Rotating breasts? Nicole's rooting reflex?
- What concerns would you have about Jenny's diet? What questions would you ask about what she is eating and drinking?
- What information could you give Jenny to help her to be successful in breastfeeding Nicole?
- If Jenny asked questions you could not answer, what would you do? How could you help Jenny get the information she needed?

CAREER PREPARATIONS

Choose the Correct Answer

Circle the letter next to the statement that best completes the sentence or answers the question.

1 Which of these routes *may not* be used to take a temperature on a child younger than 5 years of age?

a Oral
b Axillary
c Tympanic
d Rectal

2 How is the diet of a nursing mother adjusted?

a Fewer calories are needed.
b The mother needs six or more servings of milk per day.
c Food high in fats should be included.
d Chocolate and cola beverages are encouraged.

3 Which of these statements is true about bottle-fed infants?

a These babies tend to take in more air when they nurse.
b Babies fed in this way tend to have bowel movements after feedings.
c The baby may be weighed before and after the feeding to determine the amount eaten.
d The mother will want to stimulate the rooting reflex at the beginning of the feeding.

4 How do you remove formula from nipples?

a Place them in the sterilizer.
b Squeeze hot, soapy water through the nipples.
c Clean with a bottle brush.
d Wash with cool, clean water.

5 Which of the following must be reported to the nurse immediately? (Mark *all* correct answers.)

a The baby "spits up" during burping.
b The baby's bowel movement consists of hard, formed stool.
c There is redness and drainage with a foul odor coming from the baby's umbilical stump.
d The baby is flushed and perspiring.
e The baby stops crying when picked up and cuddled.
f The baby is crying all the time and putting a hand to the right ear.

6 What would be a sign of infection in the cord stump?

a A dried, blackened piece of tissue
b Redness or odor at the site
c Slight bleeding when the stump falls off
d Softening around the base of the cord

7 When cleaning the circumcision, what is applied to prevent the penis from sticking to the diaper?

a Alcohol
b Soap and water
c Powder
d Petrolatum jelly

8 When giving a bath to a baby, what is the correct temperature of the water?

a 75° to 80° F
b 98.6° F
c 90° to 100° F
d 100° to 110° F

9 What part of the body is cleaned with cotton swabs during the sponge bath?

a Nostrils
b Eyes
c Ears
d Rectum

Fill-In-The-Blanks

Fill in the word or phrase that best completes the sentence or answers the question.

10 Why is it important to keep nails short when caring for an infant?

____

11 Why is it important to respond to the cries of a baby or to feed the baby when he/she is hungry? ______________________________

12 What can you do to prevent injury if you are changing a baby on a table or sofa? ______________________________

13 What does it mean when it is said a baby is "fed on demand"? ______________

____

14 How long are bottles and other equipment boiled when sterilizing? ________

____

15 What are two methods of burping a baby?

a ____

b ____

16 What should you do if a baby has diarrhea and why? ______________

____

17 How should the genital area be cleaned if the baby has had a large bowel movement or has a rash? ______________________________

18 What is used on the cord stump to promote drying? ______________

19 What are health reasons that parents may choose to have a son circumcised?

____

20 Why are sponge baths given during the first 2 weeks of life? ____________

____

21 When you are giving a tub bath, when is the head washed? ____________

____

22 Why is it important to weigh an infant before and after breastfeeding?

____

33 Basic Emergency Care

PERSONAL EXPLORATIONS

1 Consider the following situation and answer the questions about how you would handle an emergency.

SITUATION: You are eating lunch at a fast food restaurant when a child at the next table begins to gasp for air. The mother cries out, "Jimmy is choking! Someone help me!"

- How do you think you would react to a situation like this?
- What would you say to Jimmy and his mother?
- What would you do first?
- How would you attempt to dislodge the object that is choking Jimmy?
- What would you do to prevent contracting any infection from Jimmy? What equipment might be available in the restaurant that you could use?
- How long would you continue to try to help Jimmy?

2 Consider how you would handle the following situation and answer the questions accordingly.

SITUATION: As you attempt to remove the object obstructing Jimmy's breathing, he suddenly goes limp and is unresponsive.

- How would you feel now that Jimmy is unresponsive?
- What would you do first after he becomes unresponsive?
- What would you want to check? How often?
- What changes would you make in the procedure after he becomes unresponsive?
- What concerns would you have now about infection control?
- How long would you continue to help Jimmy?

3 Consider the following situation and answer the questions about what you would do if this situation happened to you.

SITUATION: You are shopping in a local discount store. As you turn a corner into the next aisle, you find an elderly man slumped against the shelves.

- How would you feel about providing emergency care in this situation?
- What concerns would you have about infection control? What could you do to decrease risk to yourself? What equipment might be available in the store that you could use?
- What would be the first thing you would do?
- How would you position the man?
- What do you need to check first after repositioning the man?
- If you find a pulse, but no respirations, what should you do?
- If you find no pulse and no respirations, what should you do?
- How long would you continue to provide emergency care to the man?

4 Consider the following situation and answer the questions about how you would handle this emergency.

SITUATION: You are accompanying a group of 10-year-olds on a school trip to a nature preserve. Jeremy trips over a tree root and falls on a broken bottle. His arm is deeply cut and bright red blood is coming out of the wound in spurts. He is sitting on the ground crying and looks very pale. When you touch him, he is perspiring and feels cold.

- How well do you think you would handle an emergency like this? What would be the most difficult part of helping this child?
- What is the first step you should take?
- How can you best control the bleeding? What might be available to use if you were out in a nature preserve with a group of children?
- How could you best protect the wound from contamination?
- How could you protect yourself from bloodborne pathogens?
- What do his symptoms (pale, cool, perspiring) tell you? How would you help to treat this problem?

CAREER PREPARATIONS

Fill-in-the-Blanks

Fill in the word or phrase that best completes the sentence or answers the question.

1 What are the goals of first aid?

a ______

b ______

2 When you activate the EMS system, what information should you give the operator?

a ______

b ______

c ______

d ______

e ______

f ______

3 What should you do if breathing has stopped, but you still can find a heartbeat? ______

4 How do you determine unresponsiveness? ______

______

5 What three steps are done to establish breathlessness?

a L ______

b L ______

c F ______

6 Where do you check for pulselessness in an adult or older child? ______

______

7 How long do you check for pulselessness? ______

8 Where do you check for pulselessness in an infant? ______

9 What is a common reaction of a person who is choking and has an airway obstruction? ______

10 Where is the fist placed when performing the Heimlich maneuver on a person who is sitting or standing? ______

______

11 What is the purpose of the finger sweep maneuver when giving assistance to an unconscious person with an airway obstruction? ______

12 How do you attempt to remove an airway obstruction on a very obese or pregnant person? ______

13 If external hemorrhage occurs, what is the first step you should take to try to stop the bleeding? ______________________________

14 What would you do next if the bleeding is not controlled using the method identified in the previous question? ______________________________

15 What are signs of internal hemorrhage?

a ____________________

b ____________________

c ____________________

d ____________________

e ____________________

16 What emergency care should be given to a person who complains of fainting or has fainted?

a ______________________________

b ______________________________

c ______________________________

d ______________________________

e ______________________________

17 If you suspect a person has had a stroke, how will you know on which side to position him/her? ______________________________

18 When an emergency occurs, how can you protect the person's right to privacy and confidentiality? ______________________________

____

Choose the Correct Answer

Circle the letter next to the statement that best completes the sentence or answers the question.

19 When cardiac arrest occurs, how soon will permanent brain damage occur if CPR is not started?

a 1 minute
b 8 to10 minutes
c 4 to 6 minutes
d 30 to 60 seconds

20 What is the major sign of cardiac arrest?

a No pulse
b Low blood pressure
c Hemorrhage
d Flushed, warm skin

21 When should you begin CPR?

a When a person loses consciousness
b When breathing has ceased
c As soon as you find the person
d When you have determined there is no pulse and no breathing

22 When you find an adult who is unresponsive, when should you activate the EMS system?

a As soon as you determine that the person is unconscious
b After you have determined breathlessness
c After you have determined pulselessness
d After performing CPR for 1 full minute

23 Which of the following should be done during mouth-to-mouth resuscitation to an adult?

a Pinch the nostrils.
b Breathe into the person's nostrils and mouth at the same time.
c Keep the person's chin down toward the chest.
d Give chest compressions and breaths at the same time.

24 Where should you position yourself when doing chest compressions with CPR?

a At the person's head
b Straddling the person's legs
c With your shoulders directly over the chest
d At the side of the person with your elbows bent

25 What is the rate of compressions and ventilations done in one-man CPR?

a 5 compressions and 1 ventilation
b 5 compressions and 2 ventilations
c 15 compressions and 1 ventilation
d 15 compressions and 2 ventilations

26 What is the rate of chest compressions when giving CPR?

a 60 per minute
b 80 to 100 minute
c 40 to 50 per minute
d 1 compression every 10 seconds

27 Which one of the following steps would be used to prevent or treat shock?

a Set the person in a comfortable chair.
b Expose the skin of the person to allow for cooling.
c Control hemorrhage.
d Turn the head to one side.

28 Which of these steps would be correct if the person is having a seizure?

a Lay the person flat on his/her back.
b Hold arms and legs still during the seizures.
c Turn the head to one side.
d Place a soft object between the teeth of the person.

29 When a burn has occurred, which of these steps would be correct?

a Cover the wounds with clean, moist coverings.
b Apply butter or ointment to the wound.
c Remove any electric wires that are touching the person.
d Cover the wound with dry, sterile dressings.

Emergency Responses

30 In this condition the victim's signs and symptoms are:

- clutching at the throat;
- inability to breathe, speak, or cough; and
- pale and cyanotic skin.

What has occurred? ______________________
What actions should be taken?

a ____

b ____

31 In this condition, the victim's signs and symptoms are:

- low blood pressure;
- rapid and weak pulse;
- rapid respirations;
- cold, moist, and pale skin; and
- confusion.

What has occurred? ______________________
What action should be taken?

a ____

b ____

c ____

d ____

e ____

32 In Figure 33-1, identify each of the pressure points that may be used to control bleeding.

a ______________________________

b ______________________________

c ______________________________

d ______________________________

e ______________________________

f ______________________________

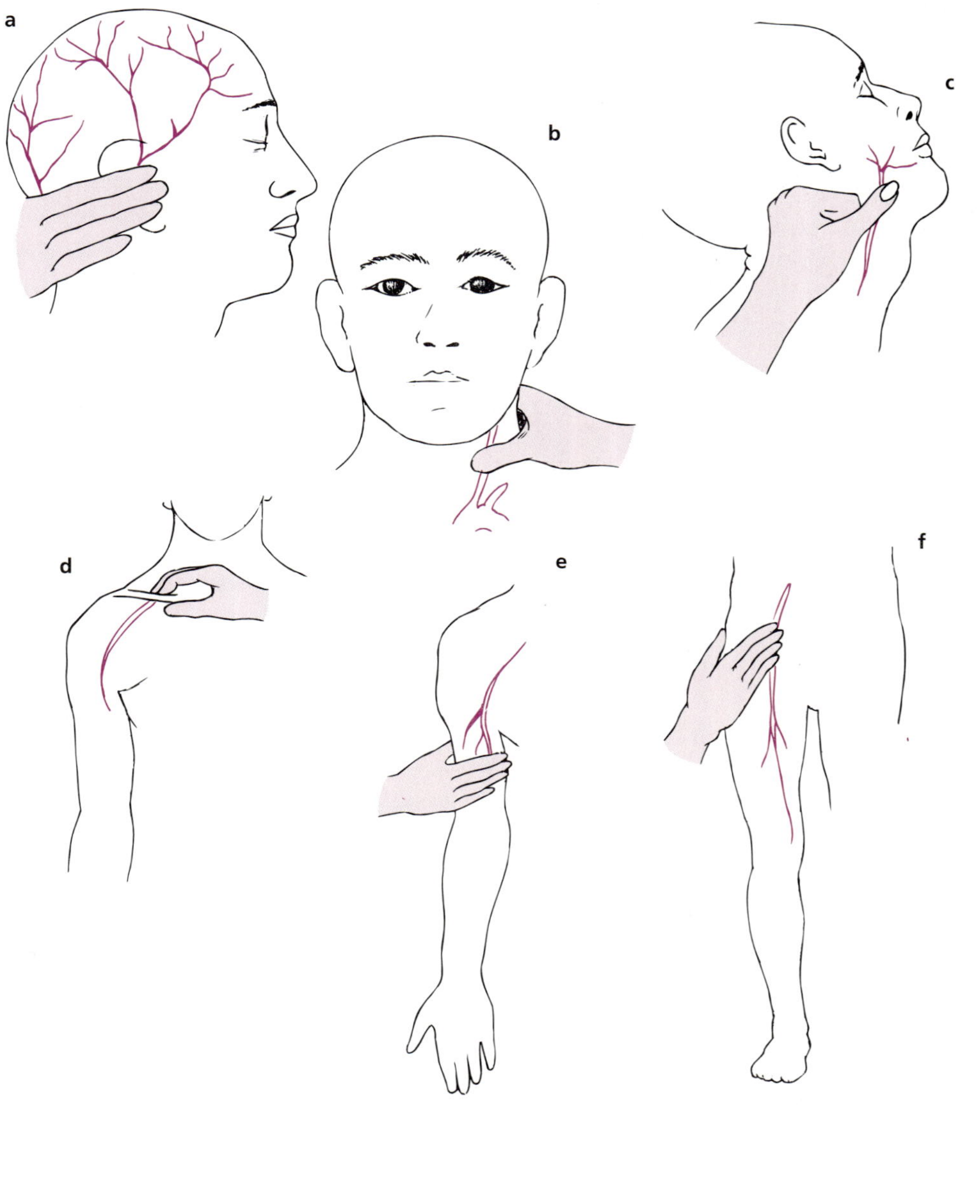

Fig. 33-1 *Pressure points to control bleeding.*

34 The Dying Person

PERSONAL EXPLORATIONS

1 Consider the following situation and answer the questions about how you would deal with the situation.

SITUATION: Mary Berk, 65, has terminal cancer. The nurse tells you the doctor has told Mrs. Berk and her family that further treatment will not stop the cancer. You have cared for Mrs. Berk during several hospital stays, and you are assigned to give her care today. When you go to her room, she tells you that she will be happy if she can live just long enough to see her grandson graduate from high school in the spring. Later when you go to her room, she is crying and saying she does not understand why this is happening to her.

- What personal beliefs about death would help you to care for a terminally ill person? What beliefs would make the assignment more difficult?
- What would you say to Mrs. Berk when she talks about her prognosis? How would this conversation make you feel?
- What effect would her present condition have on the time you spend in her room? Do you think you would want to spend more or less time with her? Why?
- What stage or stages of death does Mrs. Berk seem to be experiencing? What evidence do you have for your answer?
- What communication techniques would you use to help Mrs. Berk? How comfortable are you in using these techniques? Why do you feel as you do?

2 Consider the following situation and answer the questions about how you would feel.

SITUATION: You are on vacation for a week. When you return the nurse tells you that she is assigning you to Mrs. Berk because she has been asking for you. The nurse tells you that Mrs. Berk's condition has deteriorated, and she is very close to death. When you enter the room, Mrs. Berk seems to recognize you, but she cannot carry on a conversation. While giving care, you note physical signs that death is near.

- How would you feel about caring for someone so close to death? What difference would it make whether you know the person or not?
- How would you change your care of a dying person from caring for a person who is expected to recover? Why do you think there might be a difference?
- What kinds of signs and symptoms would you expect to observe?

3 Consider the following situation and answer the questions about how you would respond.

SITUATION: When you return from lunch, the nurse tells you that Mrs. Berk has died. She asks you to assist her with the postmortem care.

- What personal beliefs about death could affect your ability to give postmortem care?
- How would giving postmortem care to a person you knew well be easier? More difficult?
- What coping mechanisms would you use to give the postmortem care, even if it made you uncomfortable?

CAREER PREPARATIONS

Fill-in-the-Blanks

Fill in the word or phrase that best completes the sentence or answers the question.

1 What is a terminal illness? ______________________________

____

2 Where do people usually die in the United States? ______________________________

____

3 Why do many people find death frightening, morbid, or a mystery? ______________

____

4 What do children understand about death?

a Under 3 years old ______________________________

b 3 to 5 years old ______________________________

c 5 to 7 years old ______________________________

5 What two methods of communication are important in dealing with a dying person?

a ______________________

b ______________________

6 When a person is dying, why is it especially important to explain what care is being given or what activity is happening in the room? ______________________

____

7 Why should you avoid discussing topics that may upset the dying person in the room? ______________________

8 Why should you try to ask questions of the dying person that require only "yes" or "no" answers? ______________________

9 Why should oral hygiene be given frequently as death approaches?

a ______________________

b ______________________

10 What happens to circulation and body temperature as death approaches?

a Circulation ______________________

b Body temperature ______________________

11 What nursing care is especially important because of increased perspiration in the dying person?

a ______________________

b ______________________

12 What problems with elimination may occur when the person is dying?

a Bowels ______________________

b Urinary ______________________

13 How can the nursing assistant help to promote comfort when the dying person has severe pain?

a ______________________

b ______________________

c ______________________

d ______________________

14 What is the goal of hospice care? ______________________

15 What is an advance directive? ______________________

16 What right is the dying person exercising if he/she refuses treatment?

____

17 What causes the "death rattle"? ______________________

18 Why is it important to provide privacy when giving postmortem care?

____

19 When giving postmortem care, what should you do if the eyelids will not stay shut? ______________________________

20 What information is reported to the nurse when postmortem care is completed?

a ______________________________

b ______________________________

c ______________________________

Matching

Match cultural beliefs concerning death with the correct country.

a Mexico
b Vietnam
c Philippines
d Former Soviet Union
e Mainland China
f India
g Poland

21 ______ Family decides if the person will be told about a serious prognosis.

22 ______ Coins or grains of rice are placed in a dead person's mouth.

23 ______ Prayer helps the family and the person deal with anxiety and provides comfort.

24 ______ Family members stay with the dying person at all times.

25 ______ The body is not embalmed.

26 ______ The dying person is protected from knowing a poor prognosis.

27 ______ Small children are not included in death rituals.

28 ______ White clothing is worn for mourning.

29 ______ Blood transfusions and organ transplants are allowed.

30 ______ This culture believes in reincarnation.

31 ______ The person's body is placed in the home for the wake.

32 ______ This culture has an aversion to death.

Match the correct stage of death with each statement.

a Denial
b Anger
c Bargaining
d Depression
e Acceptance

33 ______ Person is sad and mourns over things that have been lost.

34 ______ Person refuses to believe death is close.

35 ______ Person takes care of unfinished business.

36 ______ Person may carry on this stage in private.

37 ______ Person may blame others for problems.

38 ______ Person may believe he/she is not dying.

39 ______ Person may make promises in exchange for more time.

Choose the Correct Answer

Circle the letter next to the statement that best completes the sentence or answers the question.

40 Which of these beliefs about death is common with younger adults?

- **a** May blame themselves when someone dies
- **b** See death as a reunion with those who have died first
- **c** Worry about who will care for and support those left behind
- **d** Welcome death as freedom from pain, suffering, and disability

41 Why are moistened eye pads applied to the eyes of a dying person?

- **a** To prevent injury
- **b** To shield the eyes from glare
- **c** To prevent a darkened room from frightening the person
- **d** To relieve pain

42 Which of these actions would be helpful to the family of a dying person? (Circle *all* correct answers.)

- **a** Stay in the room with the family and person as much as possible.
- **b** Allow family members to give care.
- **c** Give family opportunities to take a break.
- **d** Ask the family to leave when visiting hours are over.
- **e** Tell the nurse when they ask for a clergy member.

43 Which of these statements describes a living will?

- **a** It instructs a doctor not to start or to remove measures that prolong dying.
- **b** No attempts will be made to resuscitate the person.
- **c** Individual gives the right to make decisions about his/her health care to another person.
- **d** Life support measures are continued until the person is resuscitated.

44 Which of a person's rights is violated if a health care worker avoids the dying person?

- **a** Right to privacy
- **b** Right to confidentiality
- **c** Right to be free from abuse, mistreatment, and neglect
- **d** Right to protect personal possessions

35 The Home Health Care Assistant

PERSONAL EXPLORATIONS

1 Consider the following situation. Answer the questions about how you would handle the situation.

SITUATION: You are assigned to provide home care for Carol Andrews. In the initial visit to Ms. Andrews with the supervisor, you found out that she is recovering from a serious injury and needs to stay in bed as much as possible, but may be up in a chair for brief periods. When you arrive to give care the following week, Ms. Andrews asks if you will wash her hair as part of a bath. She also tells you she hates using the bedpan and asks if there is some way that she can use the bathroom.

- What assessments would you make at the beginning of this assignment? Of Ms. Andrews? Of the room and equipment?
- How would you prepare for Ms. Andrews' care? What kinds of equipment might be available in the home that you could use for care?
- What information would you want to find out from Ms. Andrews before beginning her care?
- How could you wash Ms. Andrews' hair even though she must remain in bed? How could you maintain her position and protect the bed from water? What equipment might be available in the home that you could use for this care?
- What is the first thing you should do about her request to use the bathroom? How would you find out if this is permissible? What other ways could you meet her need even if she cannot go to the bathroom?

2 Consider this situation and answer the questions about what you would do if this occurred while you were giving home care.

SITUATION: While you are at Ms. Andrews' home, her daughter, Mary Ann, arrives. The following conversation occurs:

Mary Ann: "Mother, you are just being a baby about getting better. I know if you just pushed yourself a little, you could take care of yourself. You know insurance will not cover all of the cost of these home care people. It is going to cost you a fortune just because you won't try harder to get up and move."

Mary Ann to you: "Don't you think Mother could do more if she just tried harder? She has always been a baby about a little pain. She just is not thinking about the rest of us and how much this is costing."

Ms. Andrews: "Please tell Mary Ann that I can't move without help. She just doesn't believe me. I really am trying to get over this, but it hurts so much when I try to do anything." (She begins to cry softly.)

Ms. Andrews: (After her daughter storms out of the house) "Please stay with me for a while. Mary Ann just does not understand how I hurt. She is concerned about the money because I told her I cannot help her with her bills since this happened to me. I just don't know what to do. Maybe I should push myself more. Don't tell Dr. Shah if I try to get up alone."

- What would you do when the argument begins? As it continues?
- How would you respond to the daughter's question to you? To Ms. Andrews' question?
- What would you say to Ms. Andrews when she asks you to stay? What would you do if you were scheduled at another person's home?
- How would you respond when she asks you not to tell her doctor what she is doing or planning to do?

CAREER PREPARATIONS

Matching

Match each statement with the correct category of activities performed by the home health assistant.

a Similar to duties by a nursing assistant in a health facility
b Different from duties of a nursing assistant in a health facility
c Never done by a nursing assistant
d Done only with permission from a supervisor

1 ______ Taking a person to a doctor's appointment

2 ______ Moving heavy furniture

3 ______ Meeting a person's basic needs

4 ______ Identifying safety hazards

5 ______ Shopping for groceries

6 ______ Providing transportation for a person or family

7 ______ Preparing meals

8 ______ Waxing floors

9 ______ Providing infection control

10 ______ Working alone

11 ______ Making accurate observations and documentation

12 ______ Doing laundry

13 ______ Running errands for a person or family

14 ______ Cleaning bathroom and kitchen

15 ______ Using imagination and creativity to substitute items needed for personal care

Choose the Correct Answer

Circle the letter next to the statement that best completes the sentence or answers the question.

16 Which of the following *would not* be acceptable if you were a home health care assistant?

a Going to the grocery store for the person or family
b Giving physical care without assistance
c Spending time visiting with the person and family
d Reading the instructions before using any appliance

17 Whom should you call first if a life-threatening emergency occurs?

a EMS system
b Doctor
c Supervising RN
d Family

18 Which of the following would be appropriate if a family conflict arises while you are in the home giving care?

a Leave the home immediately.
b Try to determine who is right and who is wrong.
c Enter into the conversation to attempt to settle the argument.
d Have empathy and understanding for everyone.

Reading Nutrition Labels

Read the labels in Figure 35-1, a and b, and answer the following questions about the food as prepared.

19 How many servings are in each container? a ______ b ______

20 How many calories are in each serving? a ______ b ______

21 How many grams of fat are in each serving? a ______ b ______

22 How many grams of carbohydrates are in each serving? a ______ b ______

23 How many grams of protein are in each serving? a ______ b ______

24 If the person you are caring for needs more fiber in his/her diet, which food is the better choice? a ______ b ______

25 If the person you are caring for is on a sodium-restricted diet, which food is the better choice? a ______ b ______

26 If the person you are caring for must restrict the cholesterol in his/her diet, which food is the better choice? a ______ b ______

Nutrition Facts

Serving Size 1/2 cup (118g)
Servings Per Container about 4

Amount Per Serving	
Calories 100	Calories from Fat 5
	% Daily Value*
Total Fat 1g	1%
Saturated 0g	0%
Polyunsaturated 0.5g	
Monounsaturated 0g	
Cholesterol 0mg	0%
Sodium 490mg	20%
Total Carbohydrate 16g	5%
Dietary Fiber 6g	23%
Sugars 2g	
Protein 6g	
Vitamin A 0% •	Vitamin C 0%
Calcium 4% •	Iron 8%

* Percent Daily Values are based on a 2,000 calorie diet.

a

Nutrition Facts

Serving Size 2.5 oz (70g/about 2/3 cup dry pasta and 2 tbsp sauce mix)
Servings Per Container about 2 (dry)

Amount Per Serving	As Packaged	As Prepared
Calories	270	400
Calories from Fat	50	170
	% Daily Value**	
Total Fat 6g*	10%	29%
Saturated Fat 2g	10%	26%
Cholesterol 5mg	2%	3%
Sodium 760mg	32%	39%
Total Carbohydrate 45g	15%	16%
Dietary Fiber 2g	10%	10%
Sugars 6g		
Protein 10g		
Vitamin A	2%	10%
Vitamin C	2%	4%
Calcium	10%	20%
Iron	10%	10%
Thiamin	30%	30%
Riboflavin	15%	25%
Niacin	15%	15%

* Amount as packaged. When prepared as directed, 2 Tbsp margarine and 1/2 Cup 2% milk contribute an additional 130 Calories, 13g Total Fat (3g Saturated Fat), 5 mg Cholesterol, 160mg Sodium, 3g Total Carbohydrate (3g Sugars), and 2g Protein per serving (about 1 cup).

**Percent Daily Values are based on a 2,000 calorie diet. Your daily values may be higher or lower depending on your calorie needs:

	Calories:	2,000	2,500
Total Fat	Less than	65g	80g
Sat. Fat	Less than	20g	25g
Cholesterol	Less than	300mg	300mg
Sodium	Less than	2,400mg	2,400mg
Total Carbohydrate		300g	375g
Dietary Fiber		25g	30g

b

Fig. 35-1 *Reading nutrition labels.*

Fill-in-the-Blanks

Fill in the word or phrase that best completes the sentence or answers the question.

27 Who supervises the assignments given to a nursing assistant working in the home?

a ______

b ______

28 When you are giving home care, what should you do if you have a question that needs an immediate answer? ______

29 What should you do if a conflict or problem occurs before you have completed your assignment? ______

______

30 What is your first concern when working in the home? ______

31 When is cleaning done? ______

32 What infection control practices are used when giving personal care?

a ______

b ______

c ______

33 How long should properly stored leftovers be kept? ______

34 How often should the bathroom be cleaned to provide good infection control? ______

35 What information should be recorded in the person's record?

a ______

b ______

c ______

d ______

e ______

f ______

36 What information should you record about your activities?

a ______

b ______

c ______

d ______

37 When would it be appropriate to leave your car unlocked for personal safety?

______

38 Why is it important to call in when you leave a home and when you arrive at your next assignment? ______

39 How can you use a travel size container of aerosol hair spray for personal safety? ______

36 Medical Terminology

PERSONAL EXPLORATIONS

1 Medical terms are found in magazines, newspapers, and books. After studying this chapter, you should be able to identify and define these terms. Try the following exercises to practice using this knowledge every day, not just in class.

- Go to the library and ask to see the Sunday newspaper. Usually this edition will have a section dealing with health. Look up articles in this section and write down any words you do not understand. Compare these words with the terms and word parts you have learned in this chapter. How many can you define?
- Many popular magazines have a section on health, medicines, and diseases. Look at three or four magazines in the library and see how many medical terms are used. Write down the terms that you find. How many of these were you able to define?

2 The next time you or a member of your family visit the doctor and are instructed to fill a prescription, look at what the doctor has written. Do you see any abbreviations that you learned in this chapter? What do they mean? How did this chapter help you to understand what was written?

3 Make flash cards of the prefixes, suffixes, and root words in Chapter 36 of the textbook. Put the meaning of each one on the back of the appropriate card. Work alone or with a partner and, by looking at the cards, practice identifying the correct meaning of each term.

CAREER PREPARATIONS

Crossword

Word elements

ACROSS

1. Suffix for falling, dropping
4. Prefix for small, scanty
6. Suffix for development, creation
7. Prefix for rapid, fast
9. Root for abdomen
11. Prefix for excessive
12. Root for fiber, fibrous
13. Prefix for red
14. Root for artery

DOWN

1. Suffix for exaggerated fear
2. Suffix for maintaining a constant level
3. Prefix for against
5. Suffix for puncture and aspiration of
8. Root for brain
10. Root for heart

Matching

Match the word in Column A with the correct definition in Column B.

COLUMN A	COLUMN B
1 ______ Neuralgia	**a** Difficulty urinating
2 ______ Gastrostomy	**b** Inflammation of kidneys
3 ______ Cholecystectomy	**c** Pertaining to blue coloration
4 ______ Dysuria	**d** Caused by bacteria
5 ______ Gastritis	**e** Study of the skin
6 ______ Enteric	**f** Incision into large intestine
7 ______ Bacteriogenic	**g** Instrument used to examine bronchi
8 ______ Glossitis	**h** Inflammation of the tongue
9 ______ Cyanotic	**i** Nerve pain
10 ______ Dermatology	**j** Examination of rectum with instrument
11 ______ Oophorectomy	**k** Excision of gallbladder
12 ______ Colostomy	**l** Excision of ovary
13 ______ Nephritis	**m** Incision into stomach
14 ______ Bronchoscope	**n** Inflammation of stomach
15 ______ Proctoscopy	**o** Inflammation of intestine

Fill-in-the-Blanks

Write the definition of each prefix in the space provided.

16 auto- ______________________________

17 brady- ______________________________

18 circum- ______________________________

19 dys- ______________________________

20 ecto- ______________________________

21 leuk- ______________________________

22 macro- ______________________________

23 neo- ______________________________

24 supra- ______________________________

25 uni- ______________________________

Write the definition of each root word in the space provided.

26 adeno ______

27 angio ______

28 broncho ______

29 cranio ______

30 duodeno ______

31 entero ______

32 gyneco ______

33 masto ______

34 myelo ______

35 pyo ______

Write the definition of each suffix in the space provided.

36 -asis ______

37 -genic ______

38 -ism ______

39 -oma ______

40 -phasia ______

41 -ptosis ______

42 -plegia ______

43 -megaly ______

44 -scopy ______

45 -stasis ______

Write the correct abbreviations for the following phrases or terms.

46 Abdomen ______

47 Before meals ______

48 After meals ______

49 With ______

50 Cancer ______

51 Force fluids ______

52 Discontinued ______

53 Lower left quadrant ______

54 Every day ______

55 Range of motion ______

Word Search

Identify each abbreviation and abbreviate each word or phrase. Circle or highlight the meanings and abbreviations in the puzzle.

```
N E U N I T N O C S I D R O E S S
U S R P R N A Q O A W I T H O U T
R T I O N E M O D B A B E E Q L R
S A M L O C C D A H H E I G H T O
E T B U T A L L C O R V W E L L K
M O R N I N G L Q B W E I G H T E
C X R I D C E M I A R R T Q L L V
A Y W A T E R H E A R Y H I I C E
R G R A H R G R A M V S S E E D R
E E L W E L I M M E D I A T E L Y
E N C O U R A G E M E N T F E E L
```

56 $\bar{s}$ ____________________

57 am ____________________

58 Ca ____________________

59 H_2O ____________________

60 q ____________________

61 wt ____________________

62 ht ____________________

63 w/c ____________________

64 $\bar{c}$ ____________________

65 stat ____________________

66 O_2 ____________________

67 abd ____________________

68 CVA ____________________

69 Twice a day __________

70 Complete bed rest __________

71 Nothing by mouth __________

72 When necessary __________

73 Every night at bedtime __________

74 Range-of-motion __________

75 Right Lower Quadrant __________

76 Soapsuds enema __________

77 Three times a day __________

78 Four times a day __________

79 Every other day __________

80 Left Lower Quadrant __________

81 Vital signs __________

Choose the Correct Answer

Circle the word in each group that is spelled correctly.

82 Slow heart rate

a Bradecardia
b Bradycardia
c Bradacordia
d Bradicardia

83 Difficulty in urinating

a Dysuria
b Dysurya
c Dysuira
d Disuria

84 Paralysis on one side of the body

a Hemyplegia
b Hemaplegia
c Hemoplega
d Hemiplegia

85 Opening into the ileum

a Illeostomy
b Ileostomy
c Ileastoma
d Illiostomy

86 Blue color or condition

a Cyonosis
b Cyinosis
c Cyanosis
d Cianosys

87 Opening into trachea

a Tracheastomy
b Trachiostomy
c Tracheostome
d Tracheostomy

88 Pain in a nerve

a Neuralgia
b Neuroalgia
c Nourealgia
d Neurilegia

89 Examination of a joint with a scope

a Arthoscope
b Arthroscopy
c Arethroscopy
d Artheroscope

90 Rapid breathing

a Tachepnea
b Tachypinea
c Tachypnea
d Tachypnia

91 Removal of gallbladder

a Cholecystectomy

b Cholcystectomy

c Cholicystetomy

d Cholecistectomy

Using Word Elements

The following words are made up of prefixes, root words, and suffixes. Identify each of the word elements using one of these methods:

- Circle the prefixes in black, the root words in red, and the suffixes in blue.

OR

- Highlight the prefixes in yellow, the root words in pink, and the suffixes in blue.

In the space following each word, define the word.

92 Hepatomegaly ______________________________

93 Hemiplegia ______________________________

94 Cholecystectomy ______________________________

95 Laparotomy ______________________________

96 Bradycardia ______________________________

97 Neuropathy ______________________________

98 Tachypnea ______________________________

99 Polyuria ______________________________

100 Pyorrhea ______________________________

101 Dysphagia ______________________________

102 Erythrocytopenia ______________________________

103 Leukocyte ______________________________

104 Bronchoscopy ______________________________

105 Encephalopathy ______________________________

106 Stomatitis ______________________________

Practice Final Examination

Circle the letter next to the statement that best completes the sentence or answers the question.

1 The goal of health promotion is to

a reduce the risk of illness.
b prevent diseases by healthy living and good health care.
c look for causes and cures of diseases.
d detect diseases by observing signs and symptoms.

2 Rehabilitation begins when the person

a goes home.
b can function without help.
c first receives health care.
d has had tests to diagnose the disease.

3 When working in a health care facility, to whom does the nursing assistant report?

a The doctor
b The nurse in charge
c A more experienced nursing assistant
d The nursing supervisor

4 What legal term describes the action taken when a person's freedom of movement is restricted?

a Assault
b Battery
c False imprisonment
d Invasion of privacy

5 OBRA requires that you retrain and pass a new competency test if you have not worked as a certified nursing assistant for

a 2 consecutive years.
b 5 years.
c 1 consecutive year.
d 6 months.

6 If you are asked to obtain a person's signature on an informed consent, you should

a make sure the person is mentally competent.
b refuse because this is not a nursing assistant responsibility.
c ask a family member to witness the signature.
d call the doctor to come and witness the signature.

7 The purpose of a care conference is to

a identify the medical diagnosis.
b develop or devise a person's nursing care plan for effective care.
c share the end-of-shift report.
d chart day-to-day care of the person.

8 While caring for a person, you notice that the skin feels cold and clammy. What kind of data did you use to determine this information?

a Symptoms
b Objective
c Subjective
d Touch

9 What time would you write for 5:30 PM if you are using the 24-hour clock?

a 5:30
b 1730
c 1630
d 1830

10 "A meaningful relationship" would be placed in which of Maslow's hierarchy of needs?

a Physiological
b Safety and security
c Love and belonging
d Self-esteem
e Self-actualization

11 A nursing assistant refuses to answer his/her family's questions about a friend who is hospitalized. Which of the person's rights is he/she protecting?

a Privacy
b Consideration and respect
c Confidentiality
d Informed consent

12 What is the name of the body function that burns food for heat and energy?

a Metabolism
b Digestion
c Peristalsis
d Urination

13 What type of blood vessel carries blood away from the heart?

a Artery
b Vein
c Capillary
d Vena cava

14 Which part of the brain regulates and coordinates body movement?

a Brainstem
b Cerebellum
c Cerebrum
d Hypothalamus

15 What is the major function of the thyroid gland?

a Regulates growth
b Prevents excessive loss of fluid
c Regulates metabolism
d Regulates calcium use by the body

16 What reflex causes an infant to throw the arms apart and extend the legs when a loud noise occurs?

a Moro
b Grasping
c Rooting
d Sucking

17 Developmental tasks are accomplished at various ages. At what age does a person typically accept the male or female role appropriate for one's age?

a Middle childhood (6 to 8 years)
b Late childhood (9 to 12 years)
c Adolescence (12 to 18 years)
d Young adulthood (18 to 40 years)

18 Poisonous substances may build up in the blood of an elderly person because of the aging process. Which body system is probably causing this buildup?

a Integumentary
b Respiratory
c Urinary
d Cardiovascular

19 Which type of care or living arrangement allows the caregivers of an elderly person to take a vacation or a rest?

a Adult day care center
b Respite care
c Living with family
d Independent living units

20 When a nursing home resident is asked whether a student may observe a procedure, which resident right is being met?

a Right to information
b Right to privacy
c Right to freedom from abuse, neglect, and mistreatment
d Right to freedom from restraints

21 Why should an elderly person reduce fluid intake after 5 PM?

a To increase food intake with the evening meal
b To prevent constipation
c To prevent diarrhea
d To reduce the need to urinate at night

22 If a fire occurs, which of these steps should be done first?

a Use a fire extinguisher to put out the fire.
b Close all doors and windows.
c Sound the nearest fire alarm.
d Move persons who are in danger to a safe place.

23 If you discover a person has no pulse in a hand that is restrained, the *first* thing you should do is

a call the nurse.
b massage the hand.
c cut off the restraint.
d reposition the person.

24 When paralysis occurs on one side of the body, it is called

a paraplegia.
b hemiplegia.
c quadriplegia.
d hemiparesis.

25 If the infection precautions include "Masks are worn by everyone having direct contact with the person," the type of precaution is

a blood/body fluid.
b strict.
c contact.
d acid-fast bacillus (AFB).

26 Universal precautions should be used

a only when you think a resident has an infection.
b only when you are changing soiled linens.
c only when you have open skin wounds.
d when caring for all residents at all times.

27 The Bloodborne Pathogen Standard is primarily intended to protect workers from exposure to

a acid-fast bacillus.
b *E. coli.*
c HIV and HBV.
d protozoa and fungi.

28 A hepatitis B vaccination protects the person receiving it against a disease that affects the

a liver.
b blood.
c immune system.
d urinary system.

29 How can you provide a good base of support for yourself when lifting?

a Bend from the waist.
b Stand with your feet apart.
c Stoop over with knees flexed.
d Stand with your feet together.

30 Why is logrolling used to move a person?

a Allows staff to use good body mechanics
b Keeps the spine straight at all times
c Prevents the person's head from hitting the head of the bed
d Allows all staff members to lift at the same time

31 The call light should *always* be positioned

a on the bedrail.
b attached to the pillow.
c within the resident's reach.
d On the arm of the chair.

32 If you wish to locate an item in a person's closet, you should

a wait until he/she is out of the room to search.
b tell him/her you must find the item and begin to search.
c ask him/her permission to look for the item.
d inform the nurse and have him/her look for the item.

33 When you are changing bed linens, when should you wear gloves?

a At all times
b When linens are soiled with blood, body fluids, or body substances
c When you are handling the clean linens
d Before the person has had a bath

34 Why do you raise the level of the bed when you change linens?

a So that you can use good body mechanics to prevent injury
b To prevent injury to the person in bed
c To allow space under the bed for cleaning
d So that you can keep the person in good body alignment

35 When giving oral care, why should you wear gloves?

a You will have contact with the mucous membranes.
b The gums may bleed.
c There may be harmful bacteria (pathogens) in the mouth.
d You may have small cuts on your fingers that could allow bacteria to enter your body.
e All of the above

36 What is the *most important* reason that perineal care is given at least once a day?

a To make the person more comfortable
b To prevent the growth of microorganisms that cause infection
c To prevent skin breakdown
d To remove body odors

37 Which of the following is the correct way to wash the perineal area?

a Wash from the anal area toward the urethra.
b Wash in a circular motion from the outside to the inside.
c Wash from the urethra to the anal area.
d Wash back and forth over the entire area several times.

38 A person has long hair. Which procedure *cannot* be done?

a Daily brushing and combing
b Shampooing
c Cutting the hair to remove tangles and matting
d Braiding or styling

39 Which of these statements is correct about dressing or undressing a person?

a Remove clothing from the weak side first.
b Put clothing on the weak side first.
c Put clothing on the strong side first.
d Remove clothing from the side farthest away from you first.

40 Which of these steps is correct when you change a gown for a person with an IV?

a Remove the gown from the arm with the IV first.
b Gather up the sleeve of the arm with the IV and slide it over the IV site and tubing.
c Turn off the IV and disconnect it temporarily while changing the gown.
d Put the gown on the arm without the IV first.

41 If a person is unable to dress and undress independently, where should you change the person's clothes?

a In a chair
b In the person's bed
c In the bathroom
d On a stretcher

42 Which of the following correctly describes catheter care?

a Wash the perineal area and avoid touching the catheter.
b Clean the meatus and the catheter with an alcohol swab.
c Clean the catheter from the meatus down the catheter about 4 inches with soap and water.
d Clean the catheter with soap and water, starting about 4 inches below the meatus and washing toward the perineal area.

43 Which of these actions *would not* be helpful in getting a person to void?

a Pull the curtains and close doors while the person is urinating.
b Stand next to the bed and talk quietly to the person who is urinating.
c Run water in the sink while the person is sitting on the toilet.
d Stand outside the curtain or bathroom door while the person is urinating.

44 Which of these foods would be more likely to stimulate bowel elimination?

a Pudding and jello
b Whole grain cereals and fruit
c Meat and fish
d Pretzels and potato chips

45 When you examine a person for a fecal impaction, how will you know one is present?

a Soft, formed stool is expelled.
b A hard, dry mass is felt in the rectum.
c The examination stimulates diarrhea.
d Nothing is felt in the rectum.

46 What would be an effective nursing action to relieve flatulence?

a Give an enema.
b Make sure the diet is high in vegetables.
c Have the person lie flat in bed.
d Ambulate the person or place in the sidelying position.

47 When giving an enema, what should you do if the person complains of abdominal cramping?

a Insert the tube one more inch.
b Clamp the tubing until the cramping stops.
c Discontinue the enema and report this to the nurse.
d Withdraw the tube about one inch.

48 Which of these methods would help to prevent skin breakdown around the stoma?

a Clean with alcohol wipes.
b Use an antiseptic lotion or petrolatum jelly on the skin.
c Clean the area with water and mild soap.
d Wipe with tissues until clean.

49 Why are carbohydrates important in the diet?

a To supply products for tissue growth and repair
b To provide energy and bulk for bowel elimination
c To provide energy and flavor
d To supply vitamins that are needed daily

50 What responsibility does the nursing assistant have if a person is being fed through a tube?

a To remove the tube after each feeding
b To give clear liquids by mouth
c To assist the nurse in giving feedings
d To avoid giving mouth care

51 When you take the vital signs and they have changed from a previous measurement, what should you do?

a Record the results promptly in the person's record.
b Circle the changes in red.
c Report the changes to the nurse promptly.
d Take them again in 15 minutes.

52 If the person is smoking and you need to take an oral temperature, what should you do?

a Provide oral hygiene first.
b Wait 15 minutes to take the temperature.
c Take a rectal temperature instead.
d Wait 45 minutes to take the temperature.

53 How long should you take an irregular pulse?

a 30 seconds
b 2 minutes
c 5 minutes
d 1 full minute

54 What is the purpose of a footboard?

a To prevent outward rotation of the hips and legs
b To prevent decubitus ulcers from forming on the heels
c To prevent plantar flexion
d To prevent dorsiflexion

55 Which of the following is *not* a complication of bed rest?

a Urinary incontinence
b Constipation
c Blood clots
d Pneumonia
e Contractures

56 If you move a joint during range-of-motion exercises and the person complains of pain, what should you do?

a Ask the nurse to give the person something for pain.
b Stop the movement at the point where the pain occurs.
c Stop giving range-of-motion exercises to any of the joints.
d Push slightly past the point of pain so the person will regain movement of the joint.

57 Which of the following statements does *not* describe chronic pain?

a Pain lasts longer than 6 months.
b Pain is felt at the site and in nearby areas.
c Pain may be constant or occur off and on.
d Pain remains long after healing occurs.

58 Which of these statements is true about the circadian rhythm?

a It is a method of measuring pain.
b Circadian rhythm is another name for NREM sleep.
c It is a pattern of waking and sleeping periods based on a 24-hour cycle.
d Circadian rhythm is another name for REM sleep.

59 Which of these situations with a person you are admitting should be reported to the nurse immediately?

a The person needs to void.
b The person has difficulty hearing you.
c The person complains of pain and appears to be in distress.
d The person cries and expresses a desire to go home.

60 How should you greet a new person being admitted to the facility?

a Greet the person by name. Ask if he/she prefers a certain name.
b Use the first name listed in the person's record to make the person feel at home.
c Use a short nickname that seems to fit the person such as "Gramps" or "Auntie."
d Address the person with the full name, such as "John Smith," to properly identify the person.

61 What should you do if you notice that a person being admitted is restless, agitated, and wandering?

a Tell the person to stay in the room while you go get the nurse.
b Put the person in bed with the siderails up and then go tell the nurse.
c Place the person in a chair and secure each arm with a restraint.
d Ask a family member or another nursing assistant to stay with the person while you go report this behavior to the nurse.

62 Why is a person asked to urinate before a physical examination?

- **a** Incontinence will occur during the examination if the bladder is full.
- **b** A urine specimen is always collected before the examination.
- **c** The examination will not be interrupted by a need to void.
- **d** A full bladder may cause abdominal organs to be displaced.

63 How long may ice bags or packs be left in place?

- **a** 3 to 4 hours
- **b** 15 minutes
- **c** As long as ice remains in the container
- **d** 30 minutes

64 Heat should *not* be applied to which of these areas?

- **a** Hip and knee replacements
- **b** Joints
- **c** Soft tissues
- **d** Old fractures

65 Which of these procedures may be done by a nursing assistant?

- **a** Administering oxygen therapy
- **b** Suctioning
- **c** Collecting a sputum specimen
- **d** Adjusting IV flow rate

66 Why can a portable IV pump be rolled along when the person is ambulating?

- **a** It runs on batteries when it is disconnected from the wall socket for short periods of time.
- **b** It has a very long cord that allows it to move around freely.
- **c** It can be turned off while the person is ambulating.
- **d** The IV is stopped with the clamp during ambulation.

67 When is the best time to collect a sputum specimen?

- **a** At mealtime
- **b** Early in the morning
- **c** At bedtime
- **d** After using mouthwash

68 What type of enema is given to clear the colon of feces?

- **a** Commercial enema
- **b** Oil-retention enema
- **c** Suppositories
- **d** Cleansing enema

69 When you are assigned to give coughing and deep breathing exercises, which of these actions would be incorrect?

- **a** Place the person in semi-Fowler's position.
- **b** Instruct the person to take shallow breaths.
- **c** Tell the person to support the surgical wound with a small pillow.
- **d** Tell the person to cough strongly twice.

70 What movement does the person make with the foot when you instruct him to dorsiflex the foot?

- **a** Makes circles with the toes
- **b** Points the toes downward toward the foot of the bed
- **c** Points the toes upward as in a standing position
- **d** Turns the foot from side to side

71 What is a major goal of rehabilitation?

- **a** To restore the person completely to health
- **b** To restore the person to a normal life
- **c** To restore the ability to perform activities of daily living
- **d** To restore the ability to return to the job performed before the disability occurred

72 How is feeding done if the person will never be able to swallow again?

- **a** Give only liquids by mouth.
- **b** Teach special exercises to restore swallowing.
- **c** Feed through a nasogastric tube.
- **d** Feed through a gastrostomy tube.

73 Which of these is *not* a responsibility of a nursing assistant in rehabilitation?

- **a** To perform range-of-motion exercises as instructed
- **b** To correct the person firmly when exercises are not done correctly
- **c** To give praise when even a little progress is made
- **d** To practice the task the person must perform

74 Which of these signs may indicate a person has a hearing impairment? (Circle *all* the correct answers.)

- **a** Speaking very softly
- **b** Asking for words to be repeated
- **c** Pronouncing words very clearly
- **d** Leaning forward to hear
- **e** Answering questions inappropriately
- **f** Cupping the better ear toward the speaker

75 What disease is a major cause of blindness?

- **a** Cataracts
- **b** Glaucoma
- **c** Vertigo
- **d** Otitis media

76 Which of these is *not* a responsibility of a nursing assistant?

- **a** To check the battery position in a hearing aid
- **b** To clean eyeglasses with warm water
- **c** To insert contact lenses
- **d** To speak when entering the room of a blind person

77 Which of these methods is used to take the medication used for angina?

- **a** Inhalation
- **b** Swallowing it with water
- **c** Placing it under the tongue
- **d** Injection

78 Which of the following should be avoided by a person with osteoporosis?

- **a** Bed rest
- **b** Walking
- **c** Exercise
- **d** A diet rich in calcium

79 Which of these actions would be *incorrect* when caring for a person in traction?

- **a** Not adding weights to the traction
- **b** Performing range-of-motion exercises to uninvolved body parts
- **c** Removing the weights when giving care
- **d** Having the person use the trapeze to raise the body off the bed

80 If you are caring for a person who has renal calculi, what should you do with the urine?

- **a** Measure it to keep a record of output.
- **b** Strain it to find stones.
- **c** Send it to the lab for tests.
- **d** Test it for the presence of sugar.

81 Which of these may cause mental health disorders? (Circle *all* of the correct answers.)

- **a** Inability to cope with stress
- **b** Chemical imbalances in body
- **c** Characteristics inherited from parents
- **d** Drug abuse
- **e** Social and cultural factors

82 Which of these would be present if the person has delusions of persecution?

- **a** Seeing, hearing, or feeling something that is not there
- **b** Not sleeping or taking time to tend to self-care needs
- **c** Believing that one is mistreated, abused, or harassed
- **d** Having poor judgment and morals and lacking ethics

83 When you are caring for a person with mental disorders, which of these is most important?

- **a** Being able to assess vital signs correctly
- **b** Being careful of your body language
- **c** Giving complete care well
- **d** Monitoring intake and output accurately

84 What kind of environment is helpful when a person with Alzheimer's disease is agitated?

- **a** Calm, quiet environment
- **b** Complete silence or isolation
- **c** A darkened room
- **d** An area with music and people to distract the person

85 Which of these steps would *not* be helpful in caring for a confused person?

- **a** Call the person by name each time you have contact with him/her.
- **b** Keep clocks and calendars in the person's room.
- **c** Maintain a daily routine of activities.
- **d** Explain all of the day's planned activities in the morning.

86 When a person is confused, what food substance is thought to increase restlessness, confusion, and agitation?

- **a** Fats
- **b** Caffeine
- **c** Dairy products
- **d** Salt

87 Which of these statements is *true* about sexuality and the elderly?

- **a** After menopause, women are no longer interested in having sexual relations.
- **b** A man cannot have an erection as he gets older.
- **c** Sexual relationships are psychologically and physically important to the elderly.
- **d** Orgasm may be less intense and longer in duration.

88 Which of these methods is most effective in preventing the spread of sexually transmitted diseases?

- **a** Condoms
- **b** Birth control pills
- **c** Antibiotics
- **d** Spermicidal foam

89 When a mother is breastfeeding, how is her diet adjusted?

- **a** Fewer calories are needed.
- **b** The mother needs six or more servings of milk per day.
- **c** Food high in fats should be included.
- **d** Chocolate and cola beverages are encouraged.

90 When caring for a newborn infant, what would be a sign of infection in the cord stump?

- **a** A dried, blackened piece of tissue
- **b** Redness or odor at the site
- **c** Slight bleeding when the stump falls off
- **d** Softening around the base of the cord

91 When cardiac arrest occurs, how soon will permanent brain damage occur if CPR is not started?

- **a** 1 minute
- **b** 8 to 10 minutes
- **c** 4 to 6 minutes
- **d** 30 to 60 seconds

92 When you find an adult who is unresponsive, when should you activate the EMS system?

- **a** As soon as you determine that the person is unconscious
- **b** After you have determined breathlessness
- **c** After you have determined pulselessness
- **d** After performing CPR for 1 full minute

93 What is the rate of chest compressions when giving CPR?

- **a** 60 per minute
- **b** 80 to100 minute
- **c** 40 to 50 per minute
- **d** 1 compression every 10 seconds

94 Which of these beliefs about death is common with younger adults?

- **a** May blame themselves when someone dies
- **b** See death as a reunion with those who have died first
- **c** Worry about who will care for and support those left behind
- **d** Welcome death as freedom from pain, suffering, and disability

95 Which of these statements describes a living will?

- **a** It instructs a doctor not to start or to remove measures that prolong dying.
- **b** No attempts will be made to resuscitate the person.
- **c** Individual gives the right to make decisions about his/her health care to another person.
- **d** Life support measures are continued until the person is resuscitated.

96 When you are giving care in a home, whom should you call first if a life-threatening emergency occurs?

- **a** EMS system
- **b** Doctor
- **c** Supervising RN
- **d** Family

97 Which of the following would be appropriate if a family conflict arises while you are in the home giving care?

- **a** Leave the home immediately.
- **b** Try to determine who is right and who is wrong.
- **c** Enter into the conversation to attempt to settle the argument.
- **d** Have empathy and understanding for everyone.

98 Which of these words is the correct spelling of the medical term for "difficulty in urinating"?

- **a** dysuria
- **b** dysurya
- **c** dysuira
- **d** disuria

99 Which of these words is the correct spelling of the medical term for "opening into the trachea"?

- **a** tracheastomy
- **b** trachiostomy
- **c** tracheostome
- **d** tracheostomy

100 What does "erythrocytopenia" mean?

- **a** An excess of red blood cells
- **b** Pain in the muscles
- **c** A decrease or lack of red blood cells
- **d** An increase in the number of white blood cells